I Loved You Before I Met You

I Met You

Alissa Molder

Copyright © 2016 Alissa Molder

ISBN:0-692-68977-X
ISBN-13:978-0-692-68977-6

PHOTOGRAPHY CREDIT IN ORDER OF APPEARANCE:

DEDICATION

To my baby that I haven't met yet, I love you.
With everything I am, I love you.

Little one,

I fell in love with you

without even a glance.

I'm so glad to be your mommy
and to have this chance.

This chance to raise you,
and love you everyday.
I'm so happy you're here,
in every single way.

Nothing made me happier then thinking about you, and all the wonderful things that I knew you could to do.

You could fly a rocket ship and
visit outer space.
You could fly around
all over the place.

You could be a fireman,
        saving kittens from trees.

You could be a farmer
and harvest honey from bees.

You could be a doctor,
    helping those who are sick.

You could be an athlete
who is always super quick.

You could make food
that everyone would love.

You could catch a foul ball
with your baseball glove.

Or when you are older
and are fully grown,
you could raise kids
that are your very own.

Thinking about you brought me so much joy. Even just thinking if you were a girl or a boy.

I thought of your little smile
and your fingers and toes.
I thought of your
big ears and your little nose.

I laughed as I dreamed of your quips and your charms.
I smiled as I thought about holding you in my arms.

My baby,
I love you more then you know.
I love you from the top of your head,
to the tips of your toes.

If you ever feel
sad or alone,
remember that my arms
are always your home.

No matter how old you get
or if you are far,
my love will go with you
where ever you are.

My love will stick to you like the
strongest of glue,
because I loved you
before I even met you.

The End.

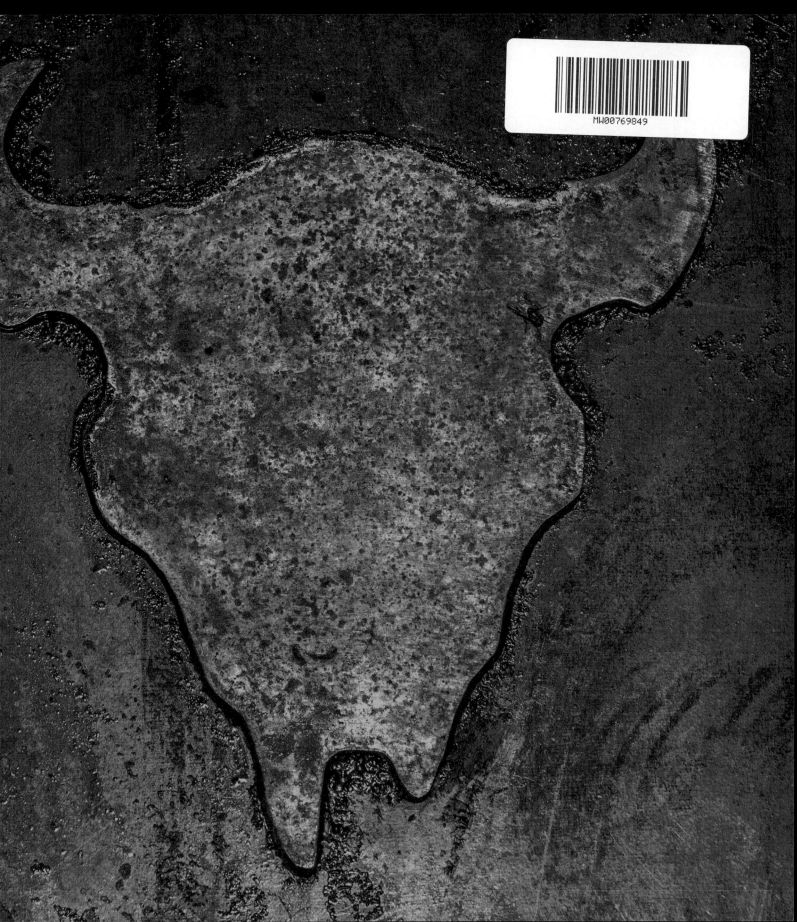

PERINI RANCH STEAKHOUSE

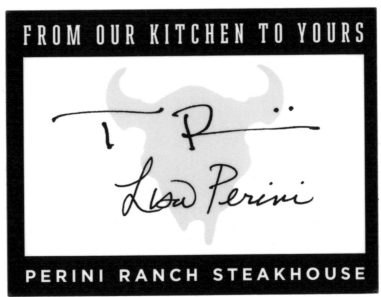

FROM OUR KITCHEN TO YOURS

PERINI RANCH STEAKHOUSE

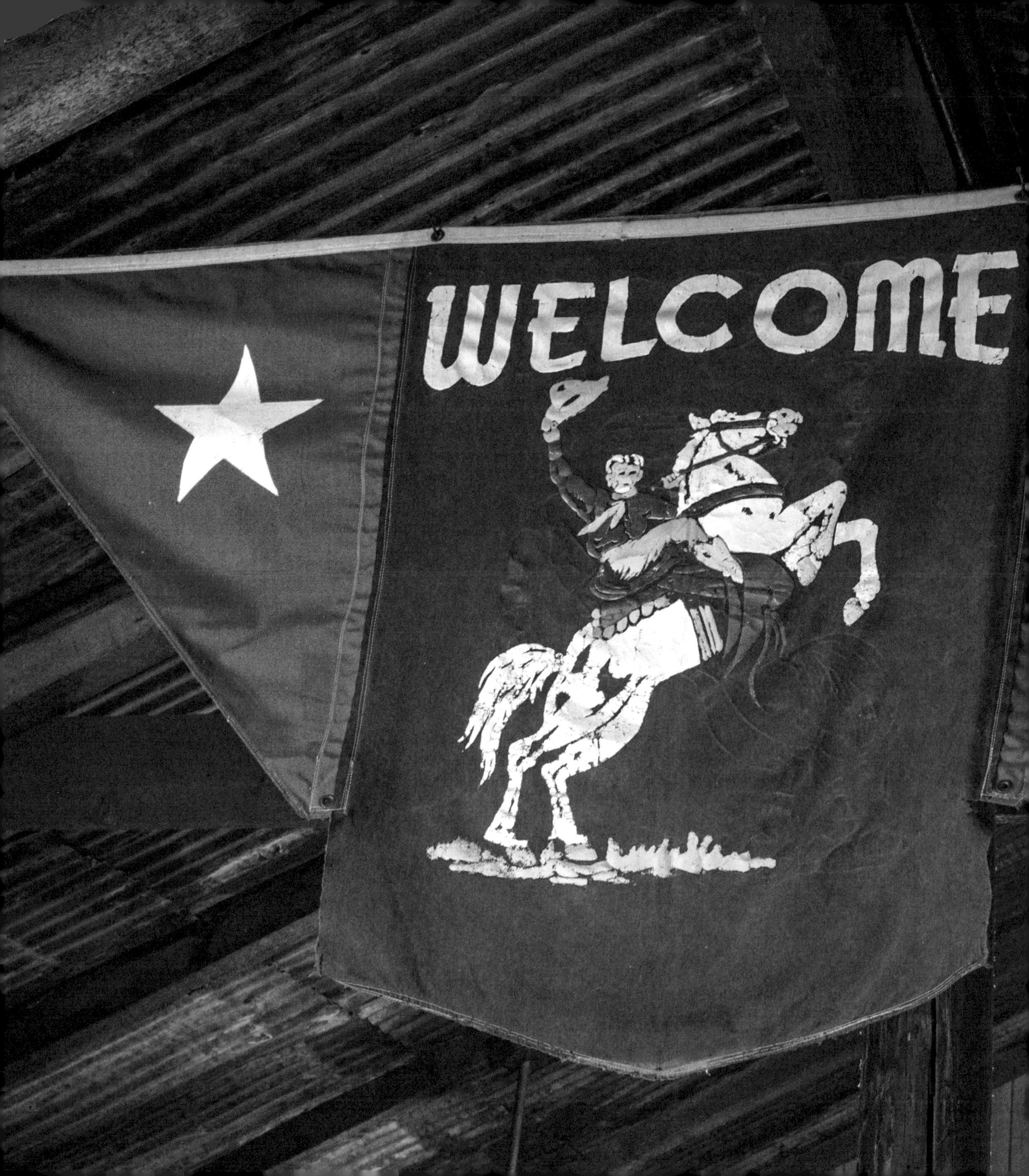
WELCOME

PERINI RANCH

STORIES AND RECIPES FOR REAL TEXAS FOOD

STEAKHOUSE

LISA AND TOM PERINI

WITH **CHERYL ALTERS JAMISON**

PHOTOGRAPHS BY **WYATT McSPADDEN**

COMANCHE
MOON
PUBLISHING
BUFFALO GAP, TEXAS

Comanche Moon Publishing
P.O. Box 728
Duffalo Gap, Texas 70500
1-800-367-1721
www.periniranch.com

Printed in U.S.A.
FIRST EDITION
ISBN: 978-1-7923-1198-7

Project Manager and Editor: Harriet Bell
Cover and Book Designer: Nancy McMillen
Production Manager: Diana Meunier

COMANCHE
MOON
PUBLISHING
BUFFALO GAP, TEXAS

To the Perini Ranch crew:

None of this would be possible without each
and every one of you. We appreciate all you
do and your dedication to our team.
Thanks for keeping our wagon wheels turning!

Lisa and Tom

CONTENTS

FOREWORD *by Cheryl Alters Jamison*

My husband, Bill, and I were pondering how to spend our 25th wedding anniversary. The timing of the auspicious event happened to be terrible. We were co-authoring a book that needed more work, a lot more work. Having a quick glass of wine with a new neighbor, we were debating a few nearby, but special, destinations that we could travel to quickly and would, just as quickly, transport us into a different realm. Our neighbor Elisa hailed from Abilene, Texas, and mentioned that she knew an extraordinary ranch and restaurant near her hometown. It had recently added some guest quarters. "The Perini Ranch Steakhouse," she enthused. We knew the name. It had a legendary, almost cult-like reputation in the culinary world—our world. Even the village where it was located sounded intriguing: Buffalo Gap, population 463.

Someone pulled up a map on a phone and the three of us squinted at the tiny dot south of Abilene. We could drive there in 6 hours. Out here in the West, that's like a cruise around the block. Bill called and booked a table at the Steakhouse and snagged us one of the new guest quarters. When our anniversary day arrived a couple of weeks later, we pulled into the ranch when the sun was low in the sky. We drove up to the coolest looking roadhouse, all weathered wood and corrugated tin. We loved it at first sight.

What we didn't know was that our neighbor had called Tom Perini, the proprietor with his wife, Lisa, and suggested that he stop by our table that evening. Tom was such a delight, full of tales tall and true, and so knowledge-able about the area that we couldn't wait to hear more. It was the first time we ever insisted that someone join us for an anniversary dinner. Our only disappointment was that Lisa was away during this initial visit to their paradise. The dinner was fabulous, real Texas food, enjoyed on that winter's night by a blazing fire. The hospitality was as warm as the night was cold. Truly, it was a magical moment.

Our first trip was followed by many others. The destination that had once seemed so remote somehow started being on our way to everywhere. Over multiple visits, we watched Lisa and Tom demonstrate their commitment to excellence, to creating the quintessential Texas experience and a community. They work hard, all the while making it look effortless. Both of us admired their devotion to each other as well. Not everyone can work with their spouse. After years of visits, together and then after Bill's death, the opportunity arose to help Lisa and Tom put together the book you are holding. What an honor to join forces with these amazing folks.

"The hospitality was as warm as the night was cold. Truly, it was a magical moment."

INTRODUCTION *by Tom Perini*

"Tom, you can do more for the beef industry by cooking beef than by raising beef."

—The late Watt Matthews, Lambshead Ranch, Albany, Texas, 1982

Watt Matthews and Tom.

That suggestion from Watt Matthews is how it all started. Soon after, Perini Ranch Steakhouse was born. But here's a little background. I grew up in Abilene, Texas, and my parents purchased a ranch in nearby Buffalo Gap in the early 1950s, where I spent a lot of time as a boy and young man. I have always loved the Perini Ranch, which sits in the saddle of the Callahan Divide, a scenic 300- to 400-foot-tall mountain range that runs south of Abilene. Long ago, bison thundered through this gap, the source of Buffalo Gap's name. The town and the ranch are nestled at the northwestern edge of the Texas Hill Country where it meets the high plains of the Llano Estacado. For a brief period in the late 19th century, Buffalo Gap was the county seat and a happening place. Through some political maneuvering, the county seat was transferred to Abilene, a booming railroad town, leaving Buffalo Gap to never grow beyond the size of a village. The 2019 population of Buffalo Gap is 463 people.

Dad passed away in 1965, when I was working in Dallas, and Mom told me, "It's time to come home to manage the ranch." I did, and also leased other ranching properties in order to run a commercial cattle operation. It was a struggle to make ends meet. Ranching and agriculture make a wonderful lifestyle, but they are difficult ways to make a living. Between weather, insects, market prices, and other acts of God, there's always a challenge. I loved being a cowboy, but it's really hard work. You can buy all the gear—the best saddle, spurs, and leggings—but that doesn't make you a cowboy.

So, I found myself spending more and more time cooking rather than on horseback. I've always enjoyed cooking and I was drawn to the kitchen. I'm a self-taught cook, not a chef, and have no culinary training. I learned to cook the hard way—with cowboys telling me my beans needed more salt! Trial and error. I was also drawn to the kitchen because of the history of chuck wagons and the food that goes along with them. Pairing Texas history with food and cooking has been a perfect career for me.

While ranching and cooking at the ranch, catering was the obvious next step. I started offering meals for Swenson Land & Cattle, Matthews, Pitchfork—all the famous, large ranches in this part of Texas. Most of the big ranches weren't using their own chuck wagons on a daily basis, so they'd ask us to come over and cook. The ranches celebrated anniversaries, horse sales, and personal parties. They would furnish the beef and mesquite; I'd bring my chuck wagon, cowboys, and the rest, and do the cooking.

By the early 1980s, cattle prices were tanking. Despite a hard-working crew, the business of running cattle was looking as profitable as the beer concession at a Baptist picnic. That's when Watt Matthews, my mentor and long-time family

"In 1983, I decided to give a roadhouse steakhouse a try and converted an old barn on our property into the Perini Ranch Steakhouse."

friend, made his game-changing observation that I should be cooking, rather than raising, beef.

In 1983, I decided to give a roadhouse steakhouse a try and converted an old barn on our property into the Perini Ranch Steakhouse. At first, the restaurant didn't even have a sign, and the interior was nothing more than a ranch cookshack. The original menu was written on a Big Chief paper tablet. I offered simple ranch food—mesquite grilled or smoked beef, burgers, ribs, and quail. I also incorporated classic cowboy cooking with some Dutch oven–baked biscuits and beans. I served unique side dishes, no French fries or baked potatoes, so we added some dishes that have become our signatures: a family dish, Zucchini Perini, and a jalapeño jelly–glazed cheesecake.

The first dozen years were tough and lean. I remember Mother loaning me enough money to make payroll. It was truly just a loan; she tracked every cent of it. In 1995, the business began to turn around, which I credit to four things. I was invited by the James Beard Foundation to cook at the Beard House in New York. Cooking at the Beard House is considered the culinary equivalent of a musician playing Carnegie Hall. While being a great honor, it was also a great expense. I decided I might be able to rationalize the cost by getting a little New York–based publicity. Before the trip, I shipped some of the restaurant's Mesquite Smoked Peppered Beef Tenderloins to key media. You'll find the whole story of this adventure on page 29, but the tenderloin ended up being selected by the *New York Times* as the year's best mail-order holiday gift. That was followed by Governor George W. Bush asking me to cater a tailgate party at the Texas Governor's Mansion in Austin for a University of Texas football game. I was in high cotton. If those events together weren't momentous enough, I also met Lisa, who was willing to marry me and my restaurant. As a bonus, she brought experience in the marketing, retail, and restaurant industries.

The Steakhouse has never advertised. Yet somehow, we've become the only dining establishment between Fort Worth and Santa Fe where you need a reservation. For the first dozen years, diners trickled in from the surrounding area. Over time, we started getting droves of day-tripping guests from Dallas and Houston, and then from all over the country, and beyond. Recently, when an enthusiastic gentleman flew in from Tokyo simply to have lunch, we were quite flattered.

We became a destination restaurant because of word of mouth and publicity from appearances on NBC's *Today* show, CBS's *The Early Show*, ABC's *Good Morning America*, and the Food Network. We've had cover stories in *Texas Monthly* and *Texas Highways*, and features in publications including *Saveur, Forbes,* and *People*. Once the *New York Times* hailed our Mesquite Smoked Peppered Beef Tenderloin as "stupendous," and "the tasting star," and, as I mentioned, named it the best holiday gift item in the country. Then Neiman Marcus and Williams-Sonoma pumped up our recognition further by carrying the tenderloins. And receiving a 2014 America's Classic Award from the James Beard Foundation, one of the greatest honors in the culinary world, brought a whole new wave of diners to Buffalo Gap.

Today, two signs point to the Steakhouse on the road winding out of Buffalo Gap. While we added air conditioning a few years back, much to the delight of our summer customers, the Steakhouse still looks timeless. Guests drive up through a live oak grove, passing a working oil field pump jack and Barba-dillo, a humongous metal armadillo sculpture crafted by noted Texas artist Joe Barrington. Our vegetable garden sits off to one side, full of tomatoes, peppers, greens, okra, asparagus, and more in season. I find all of this talk about farm-to-table restaurant cooking a bit humorous. Heck, cooking from the garden is what country folks have always done. We sometimes have so much produce that we hand out paper bags of vegetables to our guests to take home.

Our front screen door, with its welcoming vintage sign advertising Mrs Baird's bread (another Texas icon), helps set our relaxed and homey tone as it yawns open and closed. Inside, the place is all barn wood and concrete floors with a classic Western bar. A pair of fireplaces blaze with mesquite fires on cold nights and an outdoor firepit burns when an evening needs just a bit of warmth against a chill. Diners can eat on picnic tables during warm days and starlit evenings. Our staff is as genial and genuine as the setting and a big part of the restaurant's success. Our basset hounds, Gus and Jett, named after legendary Western movie characters, stop in daily on their rides around the ranch to give their own warm welcome to our guests.

We keep a small herd of longhorn cattle as part of the atmosphere. Some folks think those are our beef cattle, but they're pets, and they all have names. They're actually quite a sight, weighing in at about 1,800 pounds, with some six-foot spreads from horn to horn.

A visit to the Perini Ranch Steakhouse becomes much more than just a meal, but the food is central to the experience. Lots of the cooking has its roots in my early ranch cooking and is done outdoors on grills and smokers or in cowboy cast-iron Dutch ovens, much of it over mesquite coals. We offer a lot of beef—grilled ribeyes, sizzling fajitas, smoked prime rib, barbecued brisket, chicken-fried steak, and the quintessential green chile cheeseburger.

We are a steakhouse, but we're not just about meat. We serve really fine salads too, some with greens, some with beans. Our fried chicken and fried catfish are pretty magnificent, as are the black-eyed peas and—oh—our bread pudding, and my great-grandmother's strawberry shortcake. It's what home cooking used to be and can be again with our recipes and tips. Our food is simple, good, and celebratory with a South by Southwest or Southwest by South sensibility.

We catered numerous parties at the Texas Governor's Mansion in Austin during George W. Bush's time in that office and later during Governor Rick Perry's tenure. We catered White House celebrations for the Bushes and are honored to have arranged some of the family's personal and political events at their Crawford Ranch. At their ranch, we catered dinners for Russia's President Vladimir Putin and China's President Jiang Zemin that were top-secret affairs in the

"We keep a small herd of longhorn cattle as part of the atmosphere. Some folks think those are our beef cattle, but they're pets, and they all have names."

"We are a steakhouse, but we're not just about meat. Our food is simple, good, and celebratory with a South by Southwest or Southwest by South sensibility."

—NOTICE—
NO SERVICE WILL BE
PROVIDED AT THIS BAR
TO ANYONE ON A HORSE

planning phase. Staff members for the various presidents would often watch us prepare the food as well as taste it. One time, Lisa found out that a White House agent, tasked with observing her make pecan pies in one of our horse trailers turned kitchen, was also a pastry chef. She put him right to work. After the Putin dinner, the Russian president was asked in a press conference about the meal of Texas dishes including beef tenderloin and fried catfish. We held our collective breaths until he beamed and said it was a wonderful dinner. We also share a serious part of history with the Bush family and staff as we were at the White House on September 11, 2001, preparing to cater the Congressional Picnic (read more about this on page 85).

The kudos the Steakhouse has received, and more importantly the support of our loyal customers, have encouraged us to continue to up our game in every respect. The catering business, where it all started, has grown more sophisticated and we now have a full-scale event planning company. The theme can be anything from the most casual Texas barbecue to an elegant wedding. We travel to work with clients from California to Vermont, but we can also host parties in a variety of scenic locales here on the ranch. With this expansion, our menu options have evolved. You'll find some of those recipes here—seafood slaw, smoked salmon potato chips, and more. We have learned a lot over the years in catering, discovering what to do when our truck didn't fit under a ranch gate or when our pans were too large to fit in an oven. I love designing systems, ways to make things work more efficiently. I designed our catering kitchens from horse trailers; they are equipped with appliances as well as equipment and food and look much nicer on-site than big trucks. That old chuck wagon even fits inside one of the trailers.

Our mail-order business continues to grow, with the Mesquite Smoked Peppered Beef Tenderloins at the heart of the enterprise. Thousands of tenderloins fly out the door between Thanksgiving and Christmas, in particular. We've renovated a trio of historic structures in downtown Buffalo Gap. One is a stone cottage, now the Country Market, with local produce, kitchenware, books, and Steakhouse-themed merchandise. Across the road from the market, in a former general store owned by my family, we operate The Supper Club by Perini Ranch for private parties of up to forty guests. Our most recent enterprise, a storefront café, offers coffee, pastries, and other light meals. Out on the ranch, guests now have the option of staying in renovated classic Texas-style Guest Quarters. The Main House is an 1885-era farmhouse original to the property that can sleep five. The Camp House sleeps three. Grazing deer and turkey wander by at sunrise and sunset, but otherwise, the setting is absolutely tranquil.

Together, Lisa and I continue to build the Perini Ranch Steakhouse brand. We like to say that all of these businesses and projects are just spokes that keep our wagon wheel turning. We hope you'll enjoy our food—where it all started—whether made at home from these recipes or during a visit to Perini Ranch. Thanks for coming along for the ride as we proudly bring you our story. We're so glad you're here.

"Together, Lisa and I continue to build the Perini Ranch Steakhouse brand. We like to say that all of these businesses and projects are just spokes that keep our wagon wheel turning."

THE
COCKTAIL
HOUR

Pico de Gallo

MAKES ABOUT 2½ CUPS

1 cup diced tomatoes

½ cup diced yellow onion

1 to 3 jalapeños, seeded and minced

½ teaspoon kosher salt, or more to taste

1 teaspoon fresh lime juice

1 tablespoon chopped fresh cilantro leaves

Tortilla Chips (page 24)

Folks around here consider pico de gallo, a fresh chunky jalapeño-fueled salsa, to be the official condiment of Tex-Mex cooking. To make a quality version, start with the best vine-ripened tomatoes you can find at a farmers' market or grow your own, like we do. Take the time to cut the tomatoes and onions in similar size pieces, so you get a taste of both in every bite. Start with one jalapeño; add more as desired.

For a cocktail party, make pico de gallo, guacamole, and queso, and serve the trio with a hefty basket of homemade tortilla chips and plenty of Ranch Water and Mesquite-a-Rita cocktails. Pico de gallo can also be spooned on tacos, scrambled eggs, pinto beans, or even burgers.

Mix together the tomatoes, onion, and jalapeños in a bowl. Stir in the lime juice and salt and refrigerate for at least 30 minutes. Just before serving, mix in the cilantro and taste for salt, adding more as necessary. Serve with chips.

Guacamole

MAKES 3 CUPS

3 ripe Hass avocados, pitted and peeled

½ cup Pico de Gallo (opposite)

¼ cup minced white onion

½ teaspoon seeded and minced jalapeño

1½ tablespoons fresh lime juice

½ teaspoon kosher salt

¼ teaspoon garlic powder

Splash of Tabasco

Splash of Worcestershire sauce

Tortilla Chips (page 24)

The cocktail hour is a very special time of the day at our home. Even though we live together and work together, many days we don't see each other until we meet for drinks around 5:00 p.m. If we lose track of time, our basset hounds, Gus and Jett, remind us that it's cocktail time. We all head to the patio with a drink and snack in hand to review the day's activities and make our dinner plans. Often as not, we choose the simple delight of guacamole with warm, homemade chips. We use Hass avocados, the nubby, dark-green-almost-black variety, for their creaminess. The flesh should yield lightly when you press the fruit with your thumb.

Mash the avocados in a bowl with a large fork but leave some small chunks for texture. Gently stir in the pico de gallo, onion, jalapeño, lime juice, salt, garlic powder, Tabasco, and Worcestershire. Serve with tortilla chips within 30 minutes of preparation.

Chile con Queso

MAKES ABOUT 4 CUPS

½ pound bulk hot pork sausage

½ cup diced onion

1 cup medium Pace Picante Sauce

1 pound Velveeta, cut into 2-inch pieces

Tortilla Chips

In Texas, chile con queso—or just *queso*—is considered its own food group. Yes, queso is right up there with chili and chicken-fried steak. People are always trying to improve on this cheese and sausage dip by omitting the Velveeta or stirring in some fancy cheeses that just don't belong. Sometimes you just have to put aside any pretensions of food snobbery and go with what works.

A little-known fact about queso is that leftovers freeze beautifully, but usually there are no leftovers.

Combine the sausage and onion in a skillet over medium heat. Cook, using a wooden spoon to break up the sausage, until the sausage is brown and crisp and the onion is soft. If the sausage renders more than a tablespoon of fat, discard it. Stir in the picante sauce and Velveeta. Cook over low heat, stirring frequently, until the Velveeta is melted and the mixture is hot and bubbly. Serve the queso right from the skillet, or spoon into a heatproof bowl that can be placed on a warming tray. The queso can also be kept warm in a slow cooker. Serve with chips.

TORTILLA CHIPS

Of course, you can buy tortilla chips to go with guacamole, queso, pico de gallo, cactus salsa, and other dips, but they're easy to make and taste so much better.

Cut a dozen thin, 6-inch corn tortillas into quarters. Attach a deep-fry thermometer to the side of a deep, heavy skillet or a Dutch oven. Pour 2 inches of vegetable oil into the skillet and heat to 375°F. Set a wire baking rack over some paper towels near the stovetop. Put 6 to 8 tortilla wedges in the oil and cook for just a few seconds. As soon as the chips are crisp, but not brown, scoop them out with a slotted spoon and drain on the rack. Sprinkle with coarse salt while hot. Repeat with the remaining tortilla wedges, salting as you go. Serve in a napkin-lined basket.

Tortilla chips can be stored for a couple of days in an airtight container. Rewarm the chips on a baking sheet in a 250°F oven for a couple of minutes.

Cactus Salsa

MAKES ABOUT 4 CUPS

One 15.5-ounce jar nopales
or nopalitos, drained, rinsed,
and diced

One 6-ounce fresh nopal
(prickly pear cactus pad),
stickers removed, diced

1 cup diced fresh tomatoes

½ cup diced white onion

2 tablespoons olive oil

2 tablespoons minced
pickled jalapeño

1 tablespoon minced fresh
cilantro leaves

½ teaspoon crumbled dried
Mexican oregano

½ teaspoon kosher salt,
or more to taste

Tortilla Chips (opposite)

When we serve this exotic prickly pear salsa, it always elicits positive comments even from folks who didn't grow up in cactus country. The recipe comes from our friends at Mi Tierra Café y Panaderia, a truly iconic San Antonio restaurant since 1941. When we were served the salsa at the chef's table one evening, we became obsessed!

We like the combination of fresh cactus pads with the tangier, softer textured ones from a jar. You'll typically find both in a store that has a large selection of Mexican items. In some cases, the fresh cactus pad (a *nopal*) will be sold whole with all of its thorns removed. In larger markets, you may see huge round towers, taller than eye level, of whole nopales piled up. Some places offer fresh, already-sliced nopales (*nopalitos*). And yes, you could score a wild cactus pad in much of the American Southwest. However, those are covered in fine stickers that you probably don't want to mess with.

Combine the jarred nopales, fresh nopal, tomatoes, onion, olive oil, jalapeño, cilantro, oregano, and salt in a bowl. Taste and add more salt, if you wish. Refrigerate for 30 minutes. Serve with tortilla chips.

Real Nachos

MAKES 24 NACHOS

6 corn tortillas, cut into 4 wedges each

Vegetable oil, for frying

Approximately 1 teaspoon kosher salt

About 9 ounces (2¼ cups) shredded mild or medium Cheddar

1 or 2 fresh or pickled jalapeños, sliced into rounds or diced

Pico de Gallo (page 22)

We are not embarrassed to tell you that nachos are a staple at our house for dinner. Folks tend to think that we eat at the Steakhouse nightly, but that's not the case. Lisa loves to cook, but some nights, it just doesn't happen. Our go-to meal is often nachos, but not just a pile of chips. Tom is not a fan of those. This is the proper way to make real nachos, where each and every chip has its own generous portion of melty Cheddar and a jalapeño slice.

Warm 2 inches of oil in a large skillet over medium heat to 375° F. Set a wire baking rack over some paper towels near the stovetop. Put 6 to 8 tortilla wedges in the oil and cook for just a few seconds. As soon as the chips are crisp, but not brown, scoop them out with a slotted spoon and drain them on the rack. Sprinkle the chips with salt. Repeat to fry all the wedges.

Lay the tortilla chips on a baking sheet. Turn on the broiler. Cover each tortilla neatly with a small mound of cheese, about 1½ tablespoons, then top with a jalapeño round. Broil until the cheese just melts, 30 seconds to 1 minute. Remove immediately from the oven. Serve the nachos right away, along with some pico de gallo.

Cheddar-Pecan Cheese Straws

MAKES ABOUT 4 DOZEN

½ cup (1 stick) salted butter, at room temperature

4 ounces sharp Cheddar, shredded and at room temperature

1¼ cups all-purpose flour

½ teaspoon kosher salt

½ teaspoon cayenne

½ cup finely chopped pecans

Originally, these buttery crackers were called straws because they were piped from a pastry bag and cut into 2- to 3-inch straws. These are rounds, with the dough rolled into a log and sliced. Because of Lisa's South Carolina roots, cheese straws are a must at any gathering. Our recipe is a variation of a recipe from the Junior League of Abilene. (Yes, Texans like cheese straws, too.) You can double the recipe, bake, and store them in the freezer, so they're always on hand for cocktail hour.

Place the butter and cheese in the bowl of a stand mixer and cream on high speed for several minutes, until completely blended. Stop the mixer, scrape down the sides, and add the flour, salt, and cayenne. Beat again on medium speed until the dry ingredients are incorporated. Scrape the dough out onto a work surface. Scatter the pecans over the dough and work them into the dough.

Divide and roll the dough into two logs, about the diameter of a quarter. Roll the logs in wax paper and twist the ends. Chill thoroughly in the refrigerator for at least 2 hours or up to a week. (Well-wrapped logs can be frozen up to 1 month. Let them come to room temperature before slicing.)

Heat the oven to 350°F. Line 2 baking sheets with parchment paper.

Cut the logs into ¼-inch-thick slices. Rotate the dough one-quarter turn after slicing about a half-dozen straws, to keep the shape even, repeating as needed. Arrange the straws about ½ inch apart on the lined baking sheets. Bake for 8 to 10 minutes, just until set and golden. Serve warm or at room temperature. Store in a tin or other covered container for up to 1 week.

Praline Bacon

MAKES 10 SLICES

Vegetable oil spray

⅓ cup pecans

⅓ cup (not packed) brown sugar

10 thick slices bacon

3 tablespoons 100 percent pure cane syrup or light corn syrup

We created this sweet, smoky, salty, crunchy treat for a couple who wanted an elaborate cocktail party instead of a sit-down dinner for their wedding reception. The crisp bacon strips were arranged standing up in wooden boxes and placed on bars throughout the party site. Be sure to grind the pecans finely so they stick to the bacon, but are still recognizable as pecans. Make a double batch; they disappear in no time.

Heat the oven to 350°F. Line a baking sheet with parchment paper or a silicone mat. Spray a wire baking rack with vegetable oil spray and place it on the baking sheet.

Toast the pecans in a dry skillet over medium-low heat, stirring often so they don't burn, until they are aromatic. Set aside to cool for 5 to 10 minutes. Combine the pecans and brown sugar in a food processor and pulse until the nuts are finely chopped.

Arrange the bacon slices on the wire rack. Bake for 10 to 12 minutes. The bacon will not be fully cooked at this point. Using paper towels, blot the bacon to remove any excess fat. Brush the tops of each bacon slice well with the cane syrup. Evenly sprinkle the pecan-sugar mixture on the bacon slices. Return the bacon to the oven and bake for 15 minutes, or until the bacon is crisp and the topping has melted. Let the bacon strips sit and firm up, so they can stand without support. Serve at room temperature.

FROM THE STEAKHOUSE TO THE BEARD HOUSE

||||||||||||||||||||||||||||||||||||||||||||

In 1995, we were asked to cook dinner at the James Beard House in New York City for the James Beard Foundation's patrons. It's like an actor being nominated for an Academy Award. After we recovered from the initial shock and said yes, the reality of the expenses we would incur started to sink in. We would need to fly key staff to New York, put them up in hotels for several days, and donate all the food.

It was suggested to us that we might offset some of the cost if we could generate some Steakhouse publicity with New York media while in town. So, we shipped a few of our Mesquite Smoked Peppered Beef Tenderloins to food writers at magazines and the *New York Times* in hopes of snagging their attention. No one seemed interested until a call came from the *Times,* asking us to ship them a second tenderloin. The *Times* staffer making the request was so vague about why the newspaper wanted another one that Tom suspected someone just wanted it for their personal enjoyment. He considered not sending the tenderloin, but, in the end, shipped the beef as requested.

When another call came from someone talking about fact checking, Tom thought he was asking about checking our fax machine. After an awkward minute, it became clear that this fact-checker wanted details about our toll-free number and other mail-order specifics. Our tenderloin was a couple of days away from being named the *New York Times* mail order gift of the year! Our beef had made its way to the paper's committee overseeing the selection of the best holiday gifts. The only problem was that we had no USDA-approved facility to process the tenderloins and no mail-order system for large-scale shipping. You can bet, however, that Tom figured out both right away. He's never been seen—before or after—moving quite that quickly.

These days, we ship truckloads of Mesquite Smoked Peppered Beef Tenderloins just between Thanksgiving and the end of the year, but they are available all year long.

Beef Empanadas

MAKES 12

CHIMICHURRI

1½ teaspoons kosher salt

6 to 8 garlic cloves, minced

½ cup packed chopped fresh flat-leaf parsley leaves

½ cup packed chopped fresh oregano leaves

1 teaspoon red pepper flakes

2 tablespoons red wine vinegar

¼ cup extra virgin olive oil

DOUGH

2 teaspoons kosher salt

2 tablespoons lard, cut into about 6 smaller bits

3 to 3½ cups all-purpose flour

FILLING

½ pound well-marbled sirloin tip or tri-tip steak

½ teaspoon kosher salt

¼ teaspoon freshly ground black pepper

3 tablespoons plus 2 tablespoons unsalted butter

2 tablespoons lard

1 large onion, quartered and very thinly sliced

1½ teaspoons red pepper flakes

1½ teaspoons ground cumin

1½ teaspoons Spanish smoked paprika

2 green onions, minced, white and green portions kept separate

1 tablespoon extra virgin olive oil

2 tablespoons fresh oregano leaves, coarsely chopped

1 large hard-boiled egg, finely chopped

¼ cup pitted green olives, finely chopped

We learned to make these turnovers from Argentinian chef-restaurateur Francis Mallmann, who was a guest chef at our 2014 Buffalo Gap Wine & Food Summit. Folks in Argentina love beef and outdoor cooking as much as Texans do. The empanadas come from Argentina wine country and the recipe appears in *Seven Fires*, Mallmann's fascinating book detailing seven outdoor cooking methods. Chimichurri, a salsa-like dipping sauce with herbs, garlic, and other ingredients, can also accompany any grilled meat. The chimichurri, dough, and beef filling can be made a day or so in advance, as can the unbaked turnovers.

TO MAKE THE CHIMICHURRI: Bring ½ cup water to a boil in a small saucepan. Add the salt and stir until dissolved. Remove from the heat and allow to cool. Combine the garlic, parsley, oregano, and red pepper flakes in a medium bowl. Whisk in the vinegar, and then the olive oil, followed by the salt water. Transfer the chimichurri to a jar with a lid and refrigerate for 12 to 24 hours, so that the flavors blend. (Refrigerated chimichurri will keep for 2 to 3 weeks.)

TO MAKE THE DOUGH: Bring 1 cup water and the salt to a boil in a small saucepan over high heat. Add the lard and stir until it melts, then transfer to a large wide bowl. Allow to cool to room temperature. Using your hands, gradually add 2½ to 3 cups flour until you can gather the dough into a ball. Sprinkle ¼ cup flour on a work surface and knead the dough, adding more flour until it will not absorb any more. (You want a stiff, dry dough.) Shape the dough into a disk and wrap in plastic. Chill for at least 1 hour or up to 24 hours.

TO MAKE THE FILLING: Trim any gristle or fat around the circumference of the steak. With a knife, cut the meat into ⅛-inch cubes. Put the meat in a bowl and season with the salt and pepper.

Melt 3 tablespoons of the butter and ½ tablespoon of the lard in a skillet over medium-low heat. Add the onion and sauté until translucent and soft, 6 to 8 minutes. Don't let the onion brown. Add the red pepper flakes, cumin, paprika, and the white part of the minced green onions and sauté for 2 minutes. Turn off the heat and stir in the minced green onion tops. Season to taste with salt and pepper. Scrape the mixture into a bowl. Wipe out, dry, and return the skillet to the stovetop.

Pour the olive oil into the skillet and warm over high heat. Add the meat and cook, stirring occasionally, until it browns on all sides. Add the meat to the onion mixture. Stir in the remaining 1½ tablespoons lard until it melts, and then the oregano. Adjust the seasoning, if you wish. Chill the filling for at least 30 minutes, or up to 24 hours.

TO ASSEMBLE AND BAKE THE EMPANADAS: Heat the oven to 350°F. Spray a baking sheet with oil or cover with a silicone mat. Remove the dough, filling, and chimichurri from the refrigerator.

Cut the dough in half and cover one portion with plastic wrap. Using a rolling pin, roll out the other half on a floured work surface into an 8x22-inch rectangle. The dough should be ⅛-inch thick. With a 3½-inch biscuit cutter or a glass, cut the dough into 6 rounds. Lay the dough circles out on a work surface and cover. Repeat with the remaining dough.

Cut the remaining 2 tablespoons butter into 12 equal pieces. Divide the filling between the 12 dough rounds, placing the filling on one side of each round. Top each with equal portions of hard-boiled egg, olives, and butter. Brush the edges of each dough round with water and fold over the dough to make a half-moon. Using the back of a fork, crimp and seal the edges. Transfer the empanadas to the baking sheet.

Bake for 15 to 17 minutes, until lightly browned. Serve right away with chimichurri for dipping.

CALF FRIES

|||||||||||||||||||||||

Historically, calf fries have been a favorite at ranch events. Considered quite the delicacy, they are difficult to explain in polite company. When we passed them as an hors d'oeuvre before dinner at New York's James Beard House, some guests were surprised to learn that calf fries are bull testicles. Others preferred not to know the provenance of the tender fried bits they enjoyed.

Calf fries are available fresh during the spring and early summer (frozen the rest of the year), when cowboys brand, castrate, and vaccinate calves. Once the outer membranes are removed, Tom quarters them, dusts them in seasoned flour, and deep-fries them until golden brown. If requested in advance, we're happy to offer them at the Steakhouse or at private events.

When our co-author Cheryl shared her story of attending a ranch branding, cooking fresh testicles on a shovel over a wood fire, and then devouring them, we knew we'd found the right person to work with us on this book.

Pickled Okra with Pimento Cheese

MAKES 18

PIMENTO CHEESE

½ cup mayonnaise

6 ounces cream cheese, softened

¼ teaspoon table salt

⅛ teaspoon freshly ground black pepper

One 3- to 4-ounce jar pimentos, drained and diced

¾ pound (3 cups) shredded (on large holes of a grater) sharp Cheddar

¼ teaspoon red pepper flakes, or more to taste

One 16-ounce jar pickled okra, drained

These two iconic Southern specialties pair surprisingly well. You can buy already-made pimento cheese or make this version of Southern comfort food. The recipe yields enough pimento cheese that you'll have some left over to spread on crackers or use on sandwiches.

TO MAKE THE PIMENTO CHEESE: Cream together the mayonnaise and cream cheese in a medium bowl until well combined. Stir in the salt and pepper. Add the pimentos and Cheddar and stir together gently. You want some texture remaining. Add red pepper flakes to taste. Refrigerate, covered, for at least 30 minutes or up to several days. Makes 2½ cups.

TO FILL THE OKRA: Slice down one side of each okra pod from near tip to tail. At the broader stem end, make a small cut perpendicular to the long slit so that you have cut a "T." Gently scrape out the okra seeds. Nudge about 1 teaspoon pimento cheese into the okra and neatly mound another 1 teaspoon on top. Repeat with remaining okra and cheese, using about ¾ cup of the cheese. Serve right away or cover and refrigerate for up to several hours.

Stuffed BLTs

MAKES 2 DOZEN

2 dozen plump cherry tomatoes or other bite-size tomatoes

4 slices bacon, finely diced

3 to 4 tablespoons Buttermilk Ranch Dressing (page 56)

½ cup packed finely shredded then diced romaine or iceberg lettuce

Kosher salt

Some of our customers call these tomato poppers, since the tomatoes are stuffed with BLT fixings: Hollowed-out cherry tomatoes are filled with the classic sandwich's signature flavors. It's summer in one bite.

Slice a tiny sliver off the bottom of each tomato, so they will sit flat on a tray. Then slice off about ¼ of the tomato top. Using a small spoon, like a ¼-teaspoon measuring spoon, hollow out the tomatoes. (Tomato tops and interiors can go into salsa, soup, or tomato sauce.)

Put the diced bacon in a cold skillet. Turn the heat to medium-low and cook the bacon for 5 to 7 minutes, until brown and crisp. Remove the bacon with a slotted spoon and drain on paper towels.

Mix together 3 tablespoons of the ranch dressing with the bacon and lettuce. Salt to taste. Add the rest of the dressing to the mixture if it seems dry. Using a teaspoon, fill each tomato cavity, mounding up the filling. Serve immediately or cover with plastic wrap and refrigerate for up to several hours.

Jalapeño Bites

MAKES 24

One 8-ounce package cream cheese, at room temperature, cut into 12 pieces

6 medium jalapeños, each sliced in half lengthwise and seeded

12 thick slices bacon, cut in half

24 toothpicks

Our Jalapeño Bites represent one of our proudest success stories. Not only are they our most popular Perini Ranch Steakhouse appetizer, but they are made by a special Abilene organization, Disability Resources Inc. (DRI), a local residence for folks with intellectual disabilities. We deliver our ingredients to DRI, whose clients precisely assemble these spicy, savory bites. Every December we celebrate this successful partnership with a big party at the Steakhouse.

Heat the oven to 375°F. Line a baking sheet with parchment paper or a silicone mat.

Put a piece of cream cheese into each jalapeño half. Cut each cream cheese-filled portion in half crosswise. (This is easier than trying to fill 24 jalapeño pieces.) Wrap each quarter with a piece of bacon and secure with a toothpick. Arrange the bites on the prepared pan.

Bake for 18 to 22 minutes, until the bacon is crisp and the cream cheese is melted. Serve warm.

Spicy Pecans

MAKES 2 CUPS

STEAK RUB

2 teaspoons kosher salt

½ teaspoon coarsely ground black pepper

¼ teaspoon granulated garlic

¼ teaspoon ground dried oregano

Pinch each of granulated onion and beef bouillon powder

1 teaspoon brown sugar

¼ teaspoon cayenne

2 tablespoons salted butter

2 cups pecan halves

We've discovered that our steak rub has a multitude of uses. For instance, we use it instead of salt to coat the glass rim for our Bloody Mary. We give credit to Tom's daughter Caroline, who came up with the idea of sprinkling some rub on fresh or grilled pineapple. And then there are these steak rub-based–toasted piquant pecans to serve with cocktails.

Heat the oven to 350°F. Line a baking sheet with parchment paper or a silicone mat.

Combine the salt, pepper, garlic, oregano, onion, and bouillon powder in a bowl. Stir in the brown sugar and cayenne. Melt the butter in a skillet over medium heat. Stir in the pecans and coat them with the butter. Sprinkle in the steak rub mixture and stir until the pecans are well coated with the dry spices. Arrange the pecans in a single layer on the prepared baking sheet.

Bake for 8 to 10 minutes, then stir the nuts and bake for an additional 8 to 10 minutes, until the pecans are dry and toasted. Serve warm or at room temperature. Store in a zippered plastic bag for 2 to 3 days.

Smoked Salmon Potato Chips

MAKES ABOUT 24

One 6.5-ounce bag potato chips

4 ounces (½ cup) crème fraîche

4 ounces thinly sliced smoked salmon, cut into 1-inch pieces

6 large fresh dill sprigs, divided into 24 fronds

Creamy. Crunchy. Salty. Smooth. Sophisticated. Put these easy appetizers together at the last minute. And keep in mind that you need sturdy potato chips, such as Boulder Canyon's Sea Salt and Cracked Pepper Chips, to hold the salmon and crème fraîche.

Pour the potato chips onto a baking sheet and pick out 24 of the largest, best-looking ones. Save the rest for munching. Spoon a dollop of crème fraîche on top of each chip, followed by a square of smoked salmon. Garnish with a dill frond and serve immediately.

Fried Quail Legs

MAKES 1 DOZEN

Vegetable oil for deep-frying

2 large eggs

¾ cup whole milk

1 teaspoon table salt

1 dozen quail legs

1¼ cups all-purpose flour

¼ cup Cajun seasoning

Quail are a big deal in our part of Texas, especially in the fall when people come from all over the world to hunt the diminutive birds. We serve farm-raised quail from Bandera, Texas. You can order quail legs online or ask your butcher to order them. Each quail leg comes with the thigh attached, so you get a couple of delicious bites from each one.

Clip a deep-fry thermometer to the inside of a deep 12- or 14-inch cast-iron skillet or Dutch oven. Pour in the oil to a depth of 3 inches and bring the temperature of the oil to 350°F over medium-high heat. Line a baking sheet with paper towels. Put a wire baking rack on top of the paper towels.

Whisk together the eggs, milk, and salt in a bowl. Add the quail legs to the egg wash, stirring to coat all of them. Combine the flour and Cajun seasoning on a shallow plate. One by one, dip the quail legs lightly in the flour mixture and shake each to eliminate any excess flour.

In batches, fry the quail legs in the hot oil until golden brown, about 4 minutes. Don't crowd the pot or else the temperature of the oil will drop, and the quail legs won't be crisp. Use tongs to transfer the quail legs to the wire rack. Repeat with the remaining quail legs. Serve hot.

Marinated Shrimp

SERVES 6

2 tablespoons crab boil dry spice blend, such as Zatarain's

1 pound (26 to 30) medium shrimp, peeled, deveined, and tails removed

½ medium red onion, thinly sliced into rings

¾ cup white or apple cider vinegar

½ cup vegetable oil

¼ cup sugar

¾ teaspoon celery seed

¾ teaspoon kosher salt

2 tablespoons capers, plus 1 to 2 tablespoons caper brine

While Lisa's Lowcountry South Carolina heritage is the source of many of our seafood recipes, others come from the Texas Gulf Coast. This one evolved from a customer's Mexican ceviche recipe.

Combine the spice blend and 6 cups cold water in a large saucepan. Bring to a boil over high heat. Add the shrimp and return to a boil. As soon as the shrimp turn pink and opaque, 2 to 3 minutes, drain them in a colander and rinse under cold water for 10 seconds.

When cool enough to handle, alternately layer the shrimp and onion in a deep bowl or large jar. In another bowl, whisk together the vinegar, oil, sugar, celery seed, salt, and capers and their brine. Pour the marinade over the shrimp and onions. Cover with plastic wrap or a lid and refrigerate for at least 6 or up to 12 hours.

Arrange the shrimp with some onions and capers on serving plates or in martini glasses and serve chilled.

Mesquite-a-Rita

SERVES 1

Kosher salt

Lime wedge

1½ ounces El Jimador
Reposado tequila

1 ounce Housemade Sweet-
and-Sour Mix (below)

½ ounce Grand Marnier
orange liqueur

½ ounce Triple Sec
orange liqueur

½ ounce fresh lime juice

Lime slice

Housemade Sweet-and-Sour Mix

This will make more
than you need for 1 or
2 margaritas, but
refrigerated, it keeps
well for at least a week.

MAKES 8 OUNCES

½ cup sugar

½ cup fresh lime juice

½ cup fresh lemon juice

In a small saucepan, bring
½ cup water to a quick
boil. Stir in the sugar and
continue stirring until
the water is clear. Remove
from the heat and stir
in the lime and lemon
juices. Cover and
refrigerate until needed.

Here's our signature margarita, one we sell more of than any other drink. Multiply the recipe by the number of friends you have; you can make up to two at a time in a cocktail shaker. We use a well-priced, but high-quality, 100 percent blue agave reposada tequila that has been aged or rested for a couple of months in oak barrels. Just that slight amount of aging rounds and softens the tequila's bite, making it perfect for mixing into cocktails. We use a pair of orange liqueurs and fresh lime juice, never a pre-fab mix for this (or any of our cocktails), making it the ultimate margarita. *¡Salud!*

Place a thin layer of salt, about 1 tablespoon, on a saucer. Rub the rim of an Old Fashioned glass with the lime wedge and dip the rim into the salt. (Omit if you prefer your margarita *sin sal*, without salt.) Half-fill the glass with cracked ice.

Pour the tequila, sweet-and-sour mix, Grand Marnier, Triple Sec, and lime juice into a cocktail shaker. Cover and shake well to combine. Pour over the ice in the glass. Garnish with the lime slice and serve.

IT'S ALWAYS TEQUILA TIME IN TEXAS

||||||||||||||||||||||||||||||||||

Given the amount of tequila consumed in Texas, and the burgeoning distilled spirits industry around the state, you could be forgiven if you thought some tequila might be made here. Nope. By law, tequila has to be made in the Mexican state of Jalisco.

While a number of regulations affect its production, a tequila only has to be 51 percent blue agave to be labeled as such. The finest tequilas, though—and the only ones we serve at the Steakhouse—are 100 percent Weber blue agave. The plants, in the family of succulents, shoot out bluish pointed leaves of several feet in length, with rather threatening-looking spines or thorns along the sides and at the tips. *Jimadores*, the source of the El Jimador tequila name in our signature margarita, are men who work the fields, looking for those agaves at the perfect state of ripeness. If under- or overripe, the carbo-hydrate content will not be right for natural fermentation. They chop off the leaves to uncover the enormous heart of the plant, called a *piña* for its resemblance to a pineapple. Piñas can weigh as much as our pair of basset hounds. It's a laborious project to harvest the piñas, which are baked, mashed or shredded, and then allowed to ferment. The initial tequila produced after distillation is clear, but some are aged in American oak to add more character and a bit of color.

At the Steakhouse, we serve some terrific tequilas, including Maestro Dobel, Codigo by George Strait, Casa Dragones, and Clase Azul, to name just a few.

Mexican Martini

SERVES 1

Jalapeño-stuffed olives

1 tablespoon kosher salt

2 lime wedges

3 ounces Herradura Silver tequila or other 100 percent blue agave silver tequila

1½ ounces Cointreau orange liqueur

1½ ounces Housemade Sweet-and-Sour Mix (page 38)

1 to 2 teaspoons olive brine

It's the briny olives that make this technically a martini, rather than a margarita. They add a welcome savory note to this Austin original. The cocktail is best served straight up in a martini glass. If you like your martini a little "dirty," add the full amount of olive brine to the cocktail shaker.

Fill a martini glass with ice and add a splash of water to chill the glass. Skewer 2 or 3 olives onto a mini bamboo skewer or toothpick. Spread the salt on a saucer.

Combine the tequila, Cointreau, sweet-and-sour mix, olive brine, and a handful of ice cubes in a cocktail shaker. Cover and shake vigorously for at least 20 seconds. Dump the water and ice from the glass. Rub a lime wedge around the rim of the glass and dip the rim in the salt. Strain the martini into the glass and garnish with the skewered olives and remaining lime wedge.

Opposite page, from left to right: Mesquite-a-Rita (page 38) with lime and jalapeño garnish, Mexican Martini, and a shot of tequila.

CHEERS!

Well-made cocktails are all about the balance of top-shelf ingredients and fresh juices. Balance means measuring properly—no eyeballing—so the tequila, for instance, doesn't overpower the lime juice. For precise measuring and perfectly made cocktails, buy an inexpensive, hourglass-shaped cocktail jigger. The larger side is usually one jigger, which equals 1½ ounces; the smaller side is one-half jigger or ¾ ounce.

Below: A vintage jigger from Tom Perini's collection.

Paloma

3 ounces Patrón Silver tequila

1 ounce fresh lime juice

1 ounce agave nectar

One 12-ounce bottle Dublin Texas grapefruit soda

2 lime wheels

We love a story where the little guy triumphs. Dublin, Texas, about 100 miles east of Buffalo Gap, has a sweet history, quite literally. Its Dublin Bottling Works, dating back more than a century, was famously known for bottling the last of the cane sugar–sweetened Dr Pepper. All other Texas bottling plants had switched to cheaper corn syrup, which left Dublin as the keeper of the flame in the eyes of many loyal consumers. When it was reported that Dublin Bottling Works would succumb to using corn syrup, too, the sad news was so monumental that many of the state's television stations covered what was expected to be the end of the bottling company. Its demise, though, was greatly exaggerated, and they hold on with a line of fruity sodas, including grape, root beer, and their signature grapefruit version. Outside of the Texas distribution area, substitute another grapefruit soda, such as Jarritos.

Stir the tequila, lime juice, and agave nectar in a glass. Divide the mixture between two tall iced tea glasses. Fill each glass with ice. Top off each with grapefruit soda and garnish with a lime wheel before serving.

Ranch Water

SERVES 2

1 lime wedge and 2 lime wheels

1 tablespoon kosher salt

1½ ounces Maestro Dobel Diamante tequila

½ ounce fresh lime juice

Topo Chico or other sparkling water

This is a go-to cocktail at the Perini residence. When our friend Kelly Cannon came over one night with a bottle of Maestro Dobel Diamante, it became the signature tequila for Ranch Water, and has been ever since. Look for Topo Chico, a Mexican sparkling mineral water. If you can't find it, use the fizziest fizzy water you can find. Some evenings it goes down a little too easy . . .

Rub a lime wedge around the rim of two Old Fashioned glasses and dip the rim of each in the salt. Fill the glasses with ice.

Stir the tequila and lime juice in another glass. Divide the mixture between the glasses. Top off each with sparkling water and garnish with a wheel of lime.

TEXAS VODKA

||||||||||||||||||||||||||

In 1995, Bert "Tito" Beveridge opened the first Texas distillery since Prohibition when he started Tito's Handmade in an Austin shack. Tito's is now one of the best-selling vodkas in America and is widely available internationally. Tito continues to make the vodka in pot stills he designed after researching historic photos of pre-Prohibition distilling. Each and every batch continues to be taste-tested for consistency. As the leading force behind the Texas crafts spirit industry, he even helped rewrite state laws for distilling spirits, opening the way for the numerous other Texas distilleries of vodka, whiskey, and gin that have popped up like bluebonnets in the spring.

Tito's previous work as a geologist also helped him figure out the process for making quality vodka. His vodka is distilled with spring water that has run over our state's abundant limestone, making it much more nuanced than many mass-produced spirits. Deep Eddy and other Texas vodka producers have followed his lead. Look for these spirits to make fine cocktails or just for sipping on the rocks.

Pom-tini

SERVES 1

1½ ounces Tito's Handmade vodka

1½ ounces pomegranate juice

1½ ounces red grapefruit juice

½ ounce Housemade Sweet-and-Sour Mix (page 38)

1 lime wedge

The two fruit juices—pomegranate and red grapefruit— make the color of this cocktail a knockout.

Fill a martini glass with ice and a little water to chill it.

Combine the vodka, pomegranate juice, grapefruit juice, sweet-and-sour mix, and a handful of ice in a cocktail shaker. Cover and shake well. Discard the ice and water from the glass. Immediately strain the mixture into the glass and lightly squeeze the lime wedge into it. Garnish the rim with the lime wedge before serving.

The Perini Martini

SERVES 1

Blue cheese–stuffed olives

3 ounces Tito's Handmade vodka

½ ounce olive brine

1 teaspoon dry vermouth

There aren't too many words that rhyme with Perini, so we couldn't resist this name for our classic martini, shaken and "dirty." It's made with Tito's Handmade vodka from Austin. Corn based, rather than wheat or potato, it has a sweeter edge and mellow character, perfect for sipping. At one time, we garnished the martini with green olives stuffed with jalapeños, but at the Steakhouse we now use olives hand-filled with blue cheese.

Skewer one or two olives on a mini bamboo skewer or toothpick. Fill a martini glass with ice and a little water to chill it.

Place the vodka, olive brine, vermouth, and a handful of ice in a cocktail shaker. Cover and shake the hell out of it for at least 20 seconds. You want the shaker to become so cold you can barely hold it. Discard the ice and water from the martini glass, then immediately strain the martini into the glass and garnish with the skewered olives. Serve immediately.

Totally Texas Salty Dog

SERVES 1

1 tablespoon kosher salt

2 quarter slices red grapefruit

1½ ounces Waterloo No. 9 gin

3 ounces fresh
red grapefruit juice

By now, you might be catching onto our salty-tangy-tart cocktail theme. Waterloo gin comes from Daniel Barnes's Treaty Oak Distilling based in Dripping Springs, on the fringes of Austin. (The city's name was originally Waterloo prior to the arrival of Stephen F. Austin and his colonists.) In addition to juniper and traditional gin botanicals, distinctly Texan grapefruit, pecans, and lavender infuse the gin.

Spread the salt on a saucer. Rub the rim of a martini glass with one of the grapefruit slices and dip the rim into the salt.

Combine the grapefruit juice and gin in a cocktail shaker with a handful of ice. Cover and shake for at least 20 seconds. Strain the drink into the glass. Garnish with a grapefruit slice.

Ranch House Lemon "Aid"

SERVES 1

1½ ounces Deep Eddy Lemon
Vodka or Absolut Citron vodka

1 medium lemon, halved

Sprite

Club soda

Lemon wheel

If grown-ups ran summer lemonade stands, this is what they would offer.

Fill an iced tea glass with ice. Pour the vodka over the ice. Squeeze both halves of the lemon into the vodka. Add the

Sprite and club soda in equal measure to fill the glass, give it all a stir, and serve, garnished with a lemon wheel.

Buffalo Gap Bourbon Slush

SERVES 12 OR MORE

2 bags black tea

One 12-ounce can frozen orange juice concentrate, thawed

One 12-ounce can frozen lemonade concentrate, thawed

½ cup sugar

3½ cups cold water

½ to ¾ cup Maker's Mark or other bourbon

Orange slices and mint sprigs

Our friend and former employee Susan Cannan brought us this idea of serving a frozen bourbon slush. We especially enjoy drinking it on hot summer nights. Think of it as the ultimate slushy for grown-ups. It's easy and refreshing, but needs to be made well ahead of company's arrival. You'll want to start at least 6 hours or the day before you plan to serve, but it will keep in the freezer for days, ready to drink when you need a quencher.

Place the tea bags in a heatproof bowl. Pour 1 cup boiling water over them and allow to steep for 5 minutes. Discard the tea bags.

In a large pitcher or large bowl, depending on what will fit in your freezer, combine the tea with the orange juice and lemonade concentrates, sugar, water, and bourbon. Freeze for at least 6 hours. The alcohol will keep the mixture slushy, rather than entirely frozen.

When ready to serve, let the slush sit out for about 15 minutes. Spoon the mixture into iced tea glasses. Garnish each with an orange slice and a mint sprig and serve right away. Ahhhhhhh.

PERINI RANCH MAKER'S MARK

IIIIIIIIIIIIIIIIIIIIIIIIIIIIIIIII

In 2019, Perini Ranch Steakhouse Private Select Maker's Mark bourbon made its debut. Part of the reason we partnered with Maker's Mark was because their mission to be "Purposely Inefficient" mirrored how we think about our own businesses. Handcrafted products are difficult to make in this world of mass production, but we think it's well worth doing so. To make our Perini Ranch Steakhouse Private Select Maker's Mark, we traveled to the distillery in Loretto, Kentucky. Our blend started with a seven-year-old Maker's 46, which is aged longer in special seared French oak barrels for a bolder character, yet a still-smooth finish. Then we picked a combination of wood staves for aging the bourbon longer, so that it would pick up particular vanilla and caramel nuances. The distillery's cooperage formed our barrel on the spot and our team signed and sealed the barrel. It was ready to come home to Texas three months later.

Pomegranate Sangria

SERVES 12 OR MORE

¾ cup sugar

½ (1.5-liter) bottle Ste Genevieve (or other) Merlot

½ (1.5-liter) bottle Ste Genevieve (or other) Cabernet Sauvignon

1 cup Triple Sec orange liqueur

1½ cups pomegranate juice

1 cup fresh lime juice

1½ cups fresh orange juice

2 green apples, cored and cubed

2 oranges, 1 peeled and segmented, the other sliced to garnish glasses

Club soda, at least 12 ounces

While any Merlot or Cabernet Sauvignon can be used in this fruity sangria, ours is made with wines from Ste Genevieve Winery in West Texas, not far from historic Fort Stockton. The winery and vineyards are in the Escondido Valley appellation. We serve this in the summer and it's very refreshing.

Make a simple syrup by stirring together the sugar and ¾ cup water in saucepan over medium heat. Stir until the sugar is completely dissolved. Let the syrup cool.

Stir together the two wines, Triple Sec, fruit juices, apples, and segmented orange in a glass pitcher. Stir in the simple syrup. Refrigerate the sangria for 6 hours.

To serve, pour some sangria into a wineglass, add a splash of club soda, and garnish with an orange slice.

LISA'S LIST

||||||||||||||||||||||

We have been very fortunate to have traveled the world with Dr. and Mrs. Richard Becker of Becker Vineyards and Mr. Guy Stout, Master Sommelier and Certified Wine Educator with Southern Glazer's Wine and Spirits, tasting and studying wine. Lisa loves bringing back her discoveries and sharing them with customers as Lisa's List. It's a selection of her recent finds and special purchases, hand-written on a paper wine sack. You can usually tell where we last traveled by the appellations of the wines on Lisa's List. We truly enjoy the art of pairing wine with food, and how, when you get that right, your dining experience is enhanced. Most evenings you can find Lisa at home, cooking, and for sure, she's already selected the wine that is the perfect one to pair with dinner. Lisa has a Level 1 sommelier certificate, the introductory level of wine knowledge, which means that she's passed a series of tasting tests.

On the Steakhouse menu, we always offer eight to ten wines by the glass, as well as wines by the bottle from Texas, California, Italy, France, and just about anywhere grapes are grown. You'll find plenty of value-priced selections as well as some suggestions for splurges. You can celebrate with a bottle of Veuve Clicquot's iconic Yellow Label Champagne from France, or New Mexico's gently priced, but high-quality, sparkling wine from Gruet.

Many visitors to Texas are surprised to learn that certain regions in the Lone Star State are ideal for growing wine grapes.

At the Steakhouse, we are committed to sharing the sophisti-cated wines of Texas producers, along with all the winemaking regions of the world.

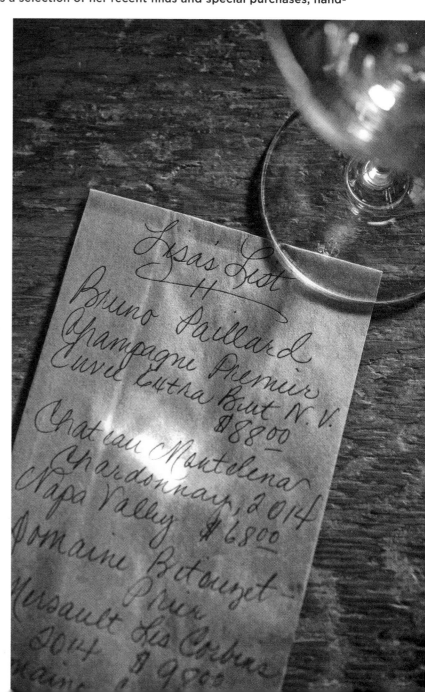

THE BUFFLO GAP
WINE & FOOD SUMMIT

||||||||||||||||||||||||||||||||||||||||||||

In 2005, we founded this wine and food event with Dr. Richard Becker of Becker Vineyards in Stonewall, Texas, along with Fess Parker of Fess Parker Winery in Los Olivos, California, who grew up in San Angelo before heading off to Hollywood for his acting career. The Summit cultivates the appreciation of fine wine and food through education and industry discussion.

In 2004, Fess was receiving an award in Austin. He flew into Abilene and picked us up, along with dear friend Jimmy Tittle. As we were flying out of Abilene, over Buffalo Gap, Fess said, "You know, Perini Ranch and Buffalo Gap are so interesting, we should do some sort of wine event. And, it should be for people who are serious about wine and food. It should be called a summit."

And, that was about it. Our conversation went on to other things. But Lisa was really intrigued with the idea, so a few days later she called Fess and asked if he was serious about his idea. When he said he was, we decided that with a Texas wine partner, we could conquer the world. Several weeks later, we met in San Antonio and were joined by Richard and Bunny Becker of Becker Vineyards. During a torrential rainstorm that afternoon, we hunkered down with lunch and lots of good wine and founded the Buffalo Gap Wine & Food Summit.

While that may sound high-falutin', it doesn't interfere with people having a grand time when we convene each April for three days under tents and in our oak grove. Along with wine experts from around the world, we bring in guest chefs, including Texas legends Stephan Pyles and Jon Bonnell and internationally recognized celebrities such as Jacques Pépin and Francis Mallmann.

Preparing to serve 250 guests at "The Great American Steakhouse Experience" at the 2019 Buffalo Gap Wine and Food Summit.

SALADS

The Ranch Salad

**BUTTERMILK
RANCH DRESSING**

½ cup buttermilk

½ cup mayonnaise

Half of a 0.4-ounce packet
Hidden Valley Original Ranch
seasoning

SALAD

3 cups torn green-leaf lettuce

3 cups torn romaine leaves

3 cups torn iceberg
lettuce leaves

18 cherry tomatoes

¼ heaping cup thinly sliced
button mushrooms

½ small red onion, thinly sliced
into half-moons and separated

Freshly ground black pepper
(optional)

When Tom opened the Steakhouse, there was one salad on the menu, and this was it! He wasn't a big fan of making too many decisions during dinner, so this one salad, served with only ranch dressing, was his solution.

Ranch dressing is arguably America's favorite condiment, and it's certainly the country's top-selling salad dressing. Nowhere is ranch dressing more beloved than here in Texas, where "buttermilk dressing" dates back as far as the 1930s, when it was documented in an appearance in a San Antonio newspaper. A decade later, the folks behind the Hidden Valley Ranch in California popularized a similar dressing. We like that version so much that it tops our classic tossed salad, which is served with the majority of our entrees.

TO MAKE THE DRESSING: Combine the buttermilk, mayonnaise, and seasoning in a jar. Cover and shake vigorously to combine. Refrigerate for 30 minutes. (Shake again before using.) Makes 1 cup. (Any leftover dressing will keep refrigerated for at least a few days.)

TO ASSEMBLE THE SALAD: Combine all the greens in a large salad bowl. Top with the tomatoes, mushrooms, and red onion. Give the dressing another shake, then dress the salad to taste. Serve from the bowl or arrange equal portions on individual salad plates. In either case, offer the pepper mill and serve.

Chopped Salad with Blue Cheese Dressing

SERVES 4 OR MORE

BLUE CHEESE DRESSING

1 cup mayonnaise

¼ cup buttermilk

¼ cup sour cream

¼ cup plus 2 tablespoons extra virgin olive oil

¼ cup white wine vinegar

1½ teaspoons minced garlic

¼ teaspoon freshly ground black pepper

2 cups Danish blue cheese crumbles

CHOPPED SALAD

4 thick slices bacon

8 cups chopped romaine or a combination of romaine and iceberg lettuce

2 Roma tomatoes, chopped

½ cup Danish blue cheese crumbles

Freshly ground black pepper

So many customers tell us that they don't like blue cheese—until they try this salad. We use Danish blue cheese, which has a mild, sweet quality. And, of course, the inclusion of bacon makes everything taste better. Today, the chopped salad gets almost as much love at the Steakhouse as our salad with ranch dressing (page 56). The dressing also makes a great dip for spicy chicken wings, quail legs (page 36), and tortilla chips (page 24).

TO MAKE THE DRESSING: Whisk together the mayonnaise, buttermilk, sour cream, olive oil, vinegar, garlic, and pepper in a bowl. Stir in the blue cheese. Makes about 3 cups. Refrigerate until needed, or up to several days.

TO MAKE THE SALAD: Put the bacon slices in a cold skillet. Turn the heat to medium-low and cook the bacon for 3 minutes on one side. Turn the bacon and cook on the other side to desired doneness. Remove the bacon with a slotted spoon and drain on paper towels. When cool enough to handle, crumble the bacon with your fingers and set aside.

Combine the lettuce, half of the bacon, and half of the tomatoes in a salad bowl. Toss with about two-thirds of the dressing. Divide the salad among serving plates. Divide the remaining bacon and tomatoes among the salads and sprinkle with the blue cheese crumbles. Serve immediately, offering additional dressing and black pepper.

Layered Avocado Salad

SERVES 6 TO 8

¼ cup plus 2 tablespoons extra virgin olive oil

3 tablespoons red wine vinegar

¼ cup grated Parmesan and Romano cheese blend

1½ tablespoons Dijon mustard

¼ cup chopped green onions

2 garlic cloves, minced

1 teaspoon kosher salt

½ teaspoon freshly ground black pepper

2 large avocados, pitted, peeled, and cubed

1 large head romaine, cut into bite-size pieces, or one 9-ounce bag romaine leaves

When it's so hot in Texas that hens lay hard-boiled eggs, this salad is sure to cool you down. We appropriated the recipe from our friends Jon and Jackie Means while visiting their H-Y Ranch. The H-Y looks out over some of the most stunning landscape of the Gila Wilderness in Grant County, New Mexico. Make the salad early in the day, pull it out of the refrigerator when you're ready to eat, and give it a toss. Add some cooked shrimp to turn it into a main course.

Combine the olive oil, vinegar, cheese, mustard, green onions, garlic, salt, and pepper in a shallow 8x10-inch serving dish. Using a fork, mix the dressing ingredients to blend well. Add the avocado and stir gently to coat with the dressing. Arrange the romaine on top of the avocado, but do not toss. Cover with plastic wrap and refrigerate for 6 to 8 hours. Toss the salad just before serving.

Cucumber-Sweet Onion Salad

SERVES 8

2 pounds unpeeled cucumbers, sliced ¼ inch thick

1 large Texas 1015 onion or other sweet onion, sliced ¼ inch thick

2 cups white vinegar

1½ cups sugar

2 tablespoons black peppercorns

2 teaspoons kosher salt

1 to 2 tablespoons chopped fresh parsley, cilantro, or a combination (optional)

Dr. Leonard Pike of Texas A&M's famous agricultural school spent years perfecting a sweet, rather than tear-inducing, onion that would grow well in Texas. Called the Texas 1015, because October 15 is the optimum planting date, this super-sweet onion has been the Texas state vegetable since 1997. Use a true sweet onion—a Texas 1015, Vidalia, or Maui. The characteristic they share is a low level of pyruvate, the naturally occurring chemical compound in onions that makes you weep. That makes the onions a perfect mate for cucumbers in this quick pickled salad. Let the vegetables soak up the tangy liquid for at least a few hours, or up to 24 hours if you have the time.

Place the cucumbers and onions in a heatproof bowl. Combine 1 cup water with the vinegar, sugar, peppercorns, salt, and herbs (if using) in a saucepan. Bring to a boil and pour over the cucumbers and onions. Stir well. Cool to room temperature. Cover and refrigerate for at least 4 hours or up to 24 hours, then use a slotted spoon to serve.

Creamy Jalapeño Coleslaw

SERVES 6

4 cups shredded green cabbage

4 cups shredded red cabbage

½ cup Italian salad dressing, such as Wish-Bone

½ cup Buttermilk Ranch Dressing (page 56)

¼ cup brine from a jar of pickled jalapeños, or more to taste

Kosher salt

Here's another one of those recipes that's more than the sum of its parts. Our late friend and well-known Tex-Mex restaurateur, Matt Martinez, came up with this tangy combo. Matt and his family have been in the restaurant business in Austin and Dallas for decades, and Matt's charm and colorful personality were a force of nature.

Combine the green cabbage, red cabbage, Italian dressing, and ranch dressing in a bowl. Toss well. Add the jalapeño liquid. Taste and add salt, and more jalapeño liquid for more tang and heat. Cover and refrigerate for 30 minutes, or up to several hours. Serve chilled.

Counter clockwise from left: Cucumber-Sweet Onion Salad, Creamy Jalapeño Coleslaw, and Country Potato Salad (page 62).

Country Potato Salad

SERVES 8

POTATO SALAD

6 slices bacon

2½ to 3 pounds unpeeled red waxy potatoes, such as Red Bliss, cut into bite-size pieces

1 teaspoon kosher salt

2 hard-boiled eggs, chopped

2 green onions, thinly sliced

DRESSING

1 tablespoon bacon drippings

½ cup mayonnaise

2 teaspoons Dijon mustard

1 to 1½ teaspoons kosher salt

¼ teaspoon freshly ground black pepper

L isa says no one likes "gloppy"—whether it's coleslaw, potato salad, or any dish made with mayonnaise or other dressing. The key to great potato salad is to keep it simple and light. Start with a smaller amount of dressing; you can always add more. Thanks to our friend Matthew Wendel for his inspiration here. Matty, as he's known, is quite a chef, and we became fast friends while he worked for President George W. Bush and First Lady Laura Bush.

TO MAKE THE SALAD: Put the bacon slices in a cold skillet. Turn the heat to medium-low and cook the bacon for 3 minutes on one side. Turn the bacon and cook on the other side to desired doneness. Remove the bacon with a slotted spoon and drain on paper towels. Carefully pour 1 table-spoon of the bacon drippings into a small dish and set aside for the dressing. When the bacon is cool enough to handle, crumble with your fingers and set aside.

Place the potatoes in a large saucepan and cover with cold water. Add the salt and bring to a boil over high heat. Reduce the heat to a simmer and cook until the potatoes are tender when pierced with a fork, 20 to 25 minutes. Drain the potatoes and transfer to a large bowl.

TO MAKE THE DRESSING: Whisk together the reserved bacon drip-pings, mayonnaise, mustard, salt, and pepper in a medium bowl.

Pour the dressing over the potatoes and gently stir in the eggs and bacon. Cover with plastic wrap and refriger-ate for a minimum of 2 hours, or up to overnight. Let the potato salad come to room temperature for 20 to 30 minutes. Stir in the green onions just before serving.

Black Bean and Roasted Corn Salad

SERVES 8

VINAIGRETTE

⅔ cup vegetable oil

2 tablespoons white or apple cider vinegar

½ teaspoon Dijon mustard

½ teaspoon kosher salt

½ teaspoon freshly ground black pepper

BEAN AND CORN SALAD

Two 15.5-ounce cans black beans, rinsed and drained

3 ears roasted or otherwise cooked corn on the cob, kernels sliced off

1 red bell pepper, seeded and diced

1 cup thinly sliced green onions

2 garlic cloves, minced

1 tablespoon minced fresh cilantro leaves

When you need a salad that won't wilt in a steamy Texas July, this one is always a good bet. It can also be served as salsa with tortillas or chips, or as an eye-catching topper for grilled chicken breasts. At the Steakhouse, we grill-roast in-season fresh ears of corn, then cut off the kernels and freeze them for use throughout the year.

TO MAKE THE VINAIGRETTE: Combine the oil, vinegar, mustard, salt, and pepper in a bowl. Whisk until well combined. Makes about ¾ cup.

TO ASSEMBLE THE SALAD: Lightly toss the beans and corn together in a serving bowl. Stir in about three-quarters of the dressing along with the bell pepper, green onions, garlic, and cilantro. Taste and add additional dressing, if desired. Refrigerate the salad for at least 30 minutes. Stir again before serving.

Avocado-Grapefruit Salad with Poppy Seed Dressing

POPPY SEED DRESSING

¾ cup vegetable oil

¼ cup white or apple cider vinegar

½ cup sugar

3 tablespoons poppy seeds

1 tablespoon Dijon mustard

½ teaspoon kosher salt

AVOCADO-GRAPEFRUIT SALAD

1 head romaine lettuce, torn into bite-size pieces

3 red grapefruits, preferably Ruby Sweet or Rio Star, peeled, membranes removed, and sectioned

2 large avocados, halved, pitted, and thinly sliced

1 small red onion, sliced into paper-thin rings

Before there were well-known Texas chefs like Stephan Pyles, Dean Fearing, and Robert Del Grande, there was Helen Corbitt. She was a chef and culinary pioneer who introduced mid-century Texas to finer foods and wine. In five cookbooks and her work at bastions like Austin's Driskill Hotel and the flagship Neiman Marcus in Dallas, she transformed Texas ingredients into dishes that are now considered classics. This combination of avocados and grapefruit sections with a dollop of a German-inspired sweet-and-sour poppy seed dressing was one of her many signature dishes. It remains a Texas favorite, and we've fine-tuned our own version. Look for Texas Ruby Sweet or Rio Star grapefruit for their superior color and sweetness from November to April.

TO MAKE THE DRESSING: Combine the oil, vinegar, sugar, poppy seeds, mustard, and salt in a quart jar. Cover and shake vigorously to combine. Makes 1½ cups. (Leftover dressing can be refrigerated for 1 week.)

TO ASSEMBLE THE SALAD: Toss the romaine with about one-quarter of the dressing and arrange in a bowl or on individual salad plates. Arrange the grapefruit and avocado slices neatly over the romaine, alternating colors. Scatter the onion slices over the top. Drizzle the salad with more dressing and serve.

Watermelon-Pecan Salad with Jalapeño Vinaigrette

SERVES 6

JALAPEÑO VINAIGRETTE

½ cup jalapeño jelly

¼ cup white vinegar

WATERMELON-PECAN SALAD

¾ cup coarsely chopped pecans

3 to 4 cups chopped arugula

5 heaping cups 1-inch-cubed watermelon

1 cup Danish blue cheese crumbles

Texas farmers produce more tons of luscious summer watermelons than those in almost every other state. In this cool, refreshing salad, tangy, slightly salty blue cheese pairs surprisingly well with the melon, pecans add crunch, and jalapeño jelly gives the whole dish a bit of sweet heat. Make the dressing and prep the other ingredients up to an hour before serving so the salad can be assembled at the last minute.

TO MAKE THE VINAIGRETTE: Combine the jelly and vinegar in a lidded jar. Cover and shake well.

TO MAKE THE SALAD: Toast the pecans in a small skillet over medium heat until fragrant, about 5 minutes.

Arrange the arugula on a platter or individual salad plates. Divide the watermelon cubes over the arugula. Shake the dressing before spooning half of it on top of the arugula and watermelon. Top with the blue cheese crumbles and pecans. Serve, passing the remaining dressing at the table. Or, toss the arugula, watermelon, blue cheese, pecans, and dressing in a bowl.

Zucchini "Carpaccio"

SERVES 6

2 medium zucchini

Kosher salt

Freshly ground black pepper

2 garlic cloves, thinly sliced

½ large lemon

3 tablespoons extra virgin olive oil

2 to 3 tablespoons pine nuts, toasted

1 tablespoon honey

1 chunk Parmigiano-Reggiano

¼ cup torn fresh mint leaves for garnish

The theme of the 2017 Buffalo Gap Wine & Food Summit was "Return to Our Roots." For the first time, we cooked Italian food for 200-plus guests to celebrate the Swiss-Italian heritage of the Perini family. Thinly sliced zucchini—use a mandoline—with pine nuts, Parmigiano-Reggiano shavings, and some top-notch olive oil are combined in this bright salad.

Using a mandoline, slice the zucchini lengthwise as thinly as possible. Place the zucchini ribbons in a colander, sprinkle well with salt, and place the colander over a plate. Let the zucchini drain, tossing occasionally, for about 30 minutes. Transfer the zucchini to paper towels and pat dry.

Arrange the zucchini in a shallow baking dish in several layers, tucking garlic slices between the ribbons. Squeeze the lemon over the zucchini, cover, and refrigerate for at least 15 minutes, or up to a couple of hours.

When ready to serve, arrange the zucchini on individual plates, decoratively curling or swirling up some of the ribbons. Drizzle with the olive oil and scatter on the pine nuts. Add a few dots of honey to each plate, then shave Parmigiano over each, garnish with mint, sprinkle with salt and pepper, and serve.

Chuck Wagon Sirloin Salad with Bacon Vinaigrette

SERVES 6

BACON VINAIGRETTE

4 slices bacon

1 tablespoon all-purpose flour

½ cup warm water

½ cup white or
apple cider vinegar

2 tablespoons sugar

½ teaspoon dried oregano

Kosher salt and freshly
ground black pepper

SIRLOIN SALAD

1- to 1¼-pounds top sirloin
steak, 1 inch thick

½ teaspoon kosher salt

1 teaspoon freshly ground
black pepper

1 red bell pepper, halved
and seeded

1 white onion, sliced into
thick rounds

2 medium heads romaine,
cut into thin ribbons

1 tablespoon minced fresh
flat-leaf parsley leaves

1 tablespoon minced fresh
basil leaves

This main dish salad sprang from our work with the Texas Beef Council. With the council, we have had the good fortune to visit many countries around the globe that import U.S. beef—Poland, Russia, Japan, Mexico, Dominican Republic, and Bermuda. We've made appearances on local TV shows, at newspaper offices, and special events, such as parties at the residences of American ambassadors in some of these countries. The salad is a great way to use any leftover steak, from sirloin to flank to flat-iron to ribeye.

TO MAKE THE VINAIGRETTE: Put the bacon slices in a cold skillet. Turn the heat to medium-low and cook the bacon for 3 minutes on one side. Turn the bacon and cook on the other side to desired doneness. Remove the bacon with a slotted spoon and drain on paper towels. Reserve the drippings in the skillet and turn the heat up to medium. Add the flour to the drippings and cook, stirring continuously, until dissolved. Continuing to stir, add the warm water, vinegar, and sugar and cook until thickened. Add the oregano and salt and pepper to taste and set aside. When the bacon slices are cool enough to handle, cut them up into small pieces and set aside.

TO GRILL THE STEAK: Fire up the grill for a two-level fire capable of cooking at the same time on both high heat (1 to 2 seconds with the hand test—page 81) and medium heat (4 to 5 seconds with the hand test). If grilling over gas or charcoal, add a half-dozen mesquite chunks to the fire shortly before placing the steak on the grill. Season the steak with the salt and pepper. Grill the steak uncovered over high heat for 2½ to 3 minutes per side. Move the steak to medium heat, turning again, and continue grilling for 2½ to 3 minutes per side for medium-rare (a total of 10 to 12 minutes). The steak should be turned a minimum of three times, more often if juices begin to pool on top.

At the same time, grill the bell pepper and onion uncovered over medium heat, turning them at least once, until tender. Plan on 8 to 10 minutes for the bell pepper and 14 to 16 minutes for the onion slices.

When the pepper is cool enough to handle, remove any loose charred skin and slice it into thin ribbons. Slice the meat diagonally across the grain into ¼-inch-thick strips. Save any juices from the meat and vegetables and add them to the dressing.

Make a bed of romaine, parsley, and basil on a platter or on individual dinner plates. Arrange the steak, bell pepper, and onion slices over the greens. Drizzle with the warm dressing, scatter the bacon pieces, and serve.

Green Beans with Walnuts and Feta

2 pounds fresh thin green beans, tipped and tailed

1 tablespoon plus ½ teaspoon Kosher salt

1 cup walnuts, coarsely chopped

¾ cup extra virgin olive oil

¼ cup white wine vinegar

2 tablespoons chopped fresh dill, plus more for garnish

1 teaspoon minced garlic

¼ teaspoon freshly ground black pepper

1 small red onion, sliced into paper-thin rounds

4 ounces crumbled feta cheese

Cooked green beans with crunchy walnuts, purplish red onion, and tangy feta cheese make an elegant salad to serve at room temperature. Dress the beans with the vinaigrette at least an hour or so ahead of serving so that the beans have some time to soak up the flavors.

Bring a large saucepan of water to a boil and add 1 tablespoon salt. Add the beans and cook until tender, 5 to 6 minutes. Immediately pour off the water and plunge the beans into an ice water bath to stop their cooking and retain their bright color. When cool, drain the beans again, and blot them with paper towels to dry the surface.

Toast the walnuts in a small skillet over medium heat until fragrant, about 5 minutes.

Combine the oil, vinegar, dill, garlic, ½ teaspoon salt, and the pepper in a large bowl. Set the vinaigrette aside.

Some 45 minutes to an hour before serving, combine the beans with the vinaigrette in a shallow bowl or on a platter and chill in the refrigerator.

A few minutes before serving, mix the walnuts, onion, and cheese into the beans. Garnish with a scattering of fresh dill and serve.

Texas Caviar

Two 15.5-ounce cans black-eyed peas, rinsed and drained

1 large tomato, diced

½ cup sliced green onions

½ cup diced red onion

1 jalapeño, seeded and finely diced

2 garlic cloves, minced

¾ cup vegetable oil

¼ cup white or apple cider vinegar

1 teaspoon minced fresh oregano leaves, or ½ teaspoon crumbled dried oregano

1 teaspoon minced fresh basil leaves, or ½ teaspoon dried basil

½ teaspoon kosher salt, or more to taste

½ teaspoon freshly ground black pepper or more to taste

Lettuce leaves, for serving

This humble black-eyed pea salad with the name "caviar" appears on picnic tables, buffets, and at Sunday suppers throughout Texas.

Combine the black-eyed peas, tomato, green onions, red onion, jalapeño, and garlic in a bowl and mix. Add the oil, vinegar, oregano, basil, and salt and pepper and toss together. Cover and refrigerate for at least 6 hours, stirring occasionally.

Before serving, drain off any excess dressing and tuck a few lettuce leaves around the peas. Serve chilled or at room temperature.

Beef Tenderloin "Carpaccio"

SERVES 6

1½ pounds Mesquite Smoked Peppered Beef Tenderloin, cut into 24 slices about ¼ inch thick, at cool room temperature

6 cups arugula

6 to 8 tablespoons extra virgin olive oil

One 6- to 8-ounce hunk Parmigiano-Reggiano

Kosher salt

2 medium lemons, each sliced into 6 wedges

Our Mesquite Smoked Peppered Beef Tenderloin is our best-known dish. (You can read about it on page 29.) The beef is sublime eaten on its own, thinly sliced and perhaps with a dab of horseradish sauce. But after some twenty-five years of promoting and selling it, we and our customers have found many other tasty ways to serve the tenderloin.

Carpaccio usually refers to uncooked meat that has been thinly sliced and topped with some dressing. One of our favorites is a salad of cooked tenderloin slices, arugula, Parmigiano-Reggiano shavings, and a drizzle of extra virgin olive oil. You can order a Perini Ranch Mesquite Smoked Peppered Beef Tenderloin (periniranch.com), ready to slice, but you'll also find a recipe on page 82 for oven-roasting a tenderloin, along with more serving ideas.

Just before serving, combine the arugula in a large bowl with 6 tablespoons olive oil.

Serve the carpaccio with all of the meat laid out on a platter and then topped with the arugula and other ingredients. With a vegetable peeler, make large shavings of Parmigiano over the greens. Drizzle with the remaining olive oil, if you wish. Scatter salt over the greens, then squeeze 1 lemon wedge over each portion. Serve with another lemon wedge garnishing each portion.

Wedding Pasta Salad

SERVES 6

8 ounces bowtie pasta

Kosher salt

DRESSING

2 tablespoons extra virgin olive oil

1 medium shallot, minced

1 teaspoon minced garlic

2 tablespoons fresh lemon juice

¼ cup grated Parmigiano-Reggiano

Kosher salt and freshly ground black pepper

VEGETABLES

1 tablespoon extra virgin olive oil

½ cup diced yellow bell pepper

½ cup diced red bell pepper

½ cup diced orange bell pepper

½ cup diced red onion

3 cups packed chopped spinach leaves

1 heaping cup halved grape tomatoes

One 8-ounce jar sliced sun-dried tomatoes in oil, not drained

2 tablespoons grated Parmigiano-Reggiano

W e were working on the wedding plans for family friends—the Kinards in Abilene—when Terri (mom of the bride) shared this flavorful and colorful pasta salad recipe. It's been served at many weddings since, and we appreciate the recipe!

Bring a large pot of water to a boil and add 1 tablespoon salt. Add the bowties and cook, stirring occasionally, until tender but still firm to the bite. Drain the bowties in a colander.

TO MAKE THE DRESSING: Combine the oil, shallot, and garlic in a bowl and let sit for 15 minutes. Whisk in the lemon juice, Parmigiano, and a couple of pinches of salt and pepper.

TO COOK THE VEGETABLES: Warm the oil in a skillet over medium heat. Add the bell peppers and red onion and sauté for 2 to 3 minutes, just until the vegetables lose their raw flavor. Stir in the spinach and grape tomatoes and remove from the heat. Add the sun-dried tomatoes and their oil to the mixture. Spoon into a large shallow bowl.

Spoon the hot pasta over the vegetables and toss to combine. Add the dressing and toss again. Scatter the 2 tablespoons Parmigiano over the salad. Cover and refrigerate for at least 1 hour, or up to overnight. Bring back to room temperature before serving.

BEEF

Cowboy Ribeye Steaks

SERVES 6 OR MORE

STEAK RUB

3 tablespoons kosher salt

1¾ teaspoons coarsely ground black pepper

½ teaspoon granulated garlic

½ teaspoon dried oregano

¼ teaspoon granulated onion

¼ teaspoon beef bouillon powder

Pinch of ground white pepper

Six 1- to 1¼-pound bone-in ribeye steaks, 1½ inches thick

teaks are celebration fare—for that big raise, a new addition to the family, or just making it through the week to another Friday night. Has any boss ever said, "You've done a great job on this project, let me take you out for a chicken breast?" Nope. Nothing quite satisfies the appetite like a beef steak, especially here in Texas. There's just nothing better than the richness and deep flavor of a well-marbled, bone-in ribeye, at least in Tom's opinion. Cut from the primal rib, the bone-in ribeye is the king of grilling steaks, known for its juiciness and flavor, more than earning its reputation as the connoisseur's cut. We were both particularly proud that *Texas Monthly* magazine, in its 2010 bucket list of sixty-three things to do in Texas before you die, implored its readers to visit the Perini Ranch Steakhouse and eat our ribeye steak. ("For a steak that tastes the way God intended, there's not a better place in Texas.") We were right up there with buying a pair of custom cowboy boots.

So, can you substitute boneless steaks? Yes, but the hefty bone contributes a significant amount of flavor. Tom says the difference between a nice restaurant and a joint is that at a joint you can pick up the bone. Perini Ranch Steakhouse is definitely a joint.

Combine all the rub ingredients in a small bowl. Using your hands, coat the steaks all over with the rub. Pack it on well. Let the steaks sit at room temperature for about 30 minutes.

Fire up the grill for a two-level fire capable of cooking first on high heat (1 to 2 seconds with the hand test— see page 81) and then on medium (4 to 5 seconds with the hand test).

If grilling over gas or charcoal, add a half-dozen mesquite chunks to the fire shortly before placing the steaks on the grill. Grill the steaks over high heat for 2½ minutes per side. Move the steaks to medium heat, turning them

again, and continue grilling for 2½ to 3 minutes per side for medium-rare. If meat juices begin to pool on the surface, turn more frequently. Serve immediately.

TEXAS STEAK MADE FAMOUS IN JAPAN

Most folks have to travel some distance to get to the Steakhouse. Would you believe that we have people fly in from Japan just to eat lunch or dinner? A few years ago, we had a crew from NHK, the PBS of Japan, come for a week and film all aspects of the Steakhouse and ranch. They put together a documentary about beef that featured three places in the world. The crew traveled to France to film a butcher, to Italy to feature the beloved *bistecca alla Fiorentina,* and to the Perini Ranch Steakhouse. We know that when we welcome our many Japanese guests, they will invariably order the bone-in ribeye because that's what the host of the program ate.

BUYING QUALITY BEEF

We serve Certified Angus Beef at the Steakhouse. The American Angus Association created the trademarked Certified Angus Beef program in cooperation with the USDA to help market its beef. Beef labeled CAB is a bit pricier, but gives the buyer assurance that the meat has been selected for meeting ten specifications of consistency in marbling and tenderness, which contribute to flavor. Only about 25 percent of Angus cattle raised in the U.S. qualify to be a part of this program. Look for CAB at your supermarket or butcher shop. The beef we use is grain finished, meaning that the cattle started their lives eating grass, but were later fed a diet of corn, sorghum, and other grains, which gives the meat a sweeter finish and more even marbling.

GRADE SCHOOLING

You've likely heard about grades of beef, particularly Prime and Choice, the top two specifications. USDA inspectors grade beef on characteristics such as marbling (the interior distribution of fat) to indicate its flavor, juiciness, and tenderness. Grading is a voluntary program, done at the behest of the meat packer, and typically requested for meat expected to be Prime or Choice. Very little meat makes Prime grade, and what does is mostly sold to restaurants, though quality meat markets today typically have a few Prime cuts. If you can, buy Certified Angus Beef which will be graded Choice or Prime. Otherwise, choose steaks that have fine, smooth intramuscular fat marbling. You'll be rewarded with great eating.

PREPPING THAT PERFECT STEAK

At the Steakhouse, once we carefully select our popular big three steaks—ribeye, strip, and filet—for their marbling, we then cut them a good 1½ inches thick. The steaks are sprinkled with a dry rub of seasonings to enhance their flavor. The next step is to build a fire and burn down the mesquite wood to white-hot coals. We sear the steaks on both sides until they're charred, crusted, and cooked to a juicy medium-rare.

PORTIONS

All our steak recipes feed you and five fortunate friends—and sometimes more. But that's a sizeable investment in meat and requires a large grill, too. It's easy to cut down each recipe for one or two servings, should you prefer. Just reduce the number of steaks and amount of rub proportionately. Also, you might choose to make the full amount of rub, just using what you need for your solo steak, and keeping the rest for your next cookout.

Strip Steaks

STEAK RUB

¼ cup kosher salt

2 teaspoons coarsely ground black pepper

¾ teaspoon granulated garlic

¾ teaspoon ground oregano

¼ teaspoon granulated onion

¼ teaspoon beef bouillon powder

⅛ teaspoon ground white pepper

Six 14- to 16-ounce boneless strip steaks, 1½ inches thick

Well-marbled strip steaks from the loin may be called New York, Kansas City, or even Delmonico strips. No matter the name, they all come from just behind the rib. A strip steak isn't as densely marbled as a ribeye or as tender as a tenderloin. However, it has a beefier flavor than both. Make friends with your butcher and ask for steaks from the center of the loin.

Combine all the rub ingredients in a small bowl. Massage each steak generously with the dry rub. Let the steaks sit at room temperature for 30 minutes.

Fire up the grill for a two-level fire capable of cooking first on high heat (1 to 2 seconds with the hand test—see page 81) and then on medium (4 to 5 seconds with the hand test). If grilling over gas or charcoal, add a half-dozen mesquite chunks to the fire shortly before placing the steaks on the grill.

Grill the steaks over high heat for 2½ minutes per side. Move the steaks to medium heat, turning them again, and continue grilling for 2½ to 3 minutes per side for medium-rare. Serve immediately.

Beef Filets with Blue Cheese Butter

BLUE CHEESE BUTTER

1 cup Danish blue cheese crumbles, at room temperature

½ cup (1 stick) salted butter, at room temperature

3 ounces cream cheese, at room temperature

2 teaspoons brine from a jar of pickled jalapeños

1 tablespoon minced fresh chives

1½ teaspoons fresh lemon juice

STEAK RUB

3 tablespoons kosher salt

1¾ teaspoons coarsely ground black pepper

½ teaspoon granulated garlic

½ teaspoon ground dried oregano

¼ teaspoon granulated onion

¼ teaspoon beef bouillon powder

Pinch of ground white pepper

Six 8-ounce center-cut tenderloin filets, 1½ inches thick

Lots of folks love a filet because it's lean and cuts like butter. But without as much marbled fat as a ribeye, filet doesn't have quite as much flavor on its own, which is why it is often served with a béarnaise sauce. We prefer to top each one with a generous slice of blue cheese butter. At the Steakhouse, we cut 8-ounce sections from the middle of the tenderloin for each diner.

TO MAKE THE BLUE CHEESE BUTTER:
Combine the blue cheese, butter, cream cheese, brine, chives, and lemon juice in a food processor. Blend until combined. Transfer the butter mixture to a piece of waxed paper and roll the butter up in the paper into a 1-inch log. Refrigerate or freeze until needed.

TO MAKE THE RUB:
Combine all the rub ingredients in a small bowl.

Massage each filet generously with the rub. Let the steaks sit at room temperature for 30 minutes.

Fire up the grill for a two-level fire capable of cooking both on high heat (1 to 2 seconds with the hand test—see page 81) and on medium (4 to 5 seconds with the hand test). For the best flavor, if cooking over gas or charcoal, add a half-dozen mesquite chunks to the fire shortly before placing the steaks on the grill.

Grill the filets uncovered over high heat for 1½ minutes per side. Move the filets to medium heat, turning them again, and continue grilling for 3½ to 4 minutes more per side for medium-rare doneness. Turn three times for grill marks. Serve immediately with a slice of blue cheese butter on top of each filet.

FIRING UP THE GRILL

||||||||||||||||||||||||||||||||||||||||||||||||

Ever watched a group of guys standing around a hot fire while drinking beer, but ignoring the steaks on the grill? We'd hate to have them grilling our steaks. Grilling steaks to the right doneness requires your full attention and some basic skills. Like anything else, the more you do it, the easier it becomes and the better your steaks will be.

Knowing how to build a proper fire and how to control the heat are the first steps. Are you grilling or smoking? The main temperature variable is the quantity of fuel you use, which should always be relative to the size of the grill and the amount and type of food you're cooking.

Whether we are grilling, smoking, or cooking serious low-and-slow barbecue, we cook with mesquite wood because it's always been plentiful around these parts. These days, chefs grill with mesquite all over the country, but when Tom started this, it was considered "way out there." For all outdoor cooking, you want to burn a hardwood, like mesquite or oak, not resinous pine or cedar.

For grilling steaks or chops, we burn down fireplace-size mesquite logs to a certain level, but want active flames and high heat right under the meat. For smoked prime rib roast, we cook directly, but at a lower heat level—about 325°F—and over coals. For real barbecue, such as tough-as-a-blacksmith's-anvil pork ribs or beef brisket, the meat needs longer and lower cooking—250°F to 275°F—to develop succulence and tenderness under a coating of dried spices.

When we cater an event, we burn down logs in barrels we bring to the event (photo at right); the process always attracts the curious. We keep it behind the scenes at the Steakhouse so that no one singes their eyebrows or barbecues their boots.

We recommend using a charcoal chimney to start a fire. In a standard 22½-inch kettle-style grill, light 1½ charcoal-chimney loads of briquettes, lump charcoal, or hardwood chunks for four to six serious steaks. Briquettes reach a prime cooking temperature when they start to turn ashen, usually about 30 minutes after you light them. Lump charcoal and hardwood chunks usually ignite faster, get hotter, and burn more quickly. With any of the fuels, you can bump up the heat by bunching the coals together or opening the vents fully, or, if your grill provides the means, moving the food closer to the fire. To reduce the temperature, spread the coals apart, close or partially close the vents, or increase the distance between the food and the fire.

THE TWO-LEVEL FIRE

Thick steaks grill best on a two-level fire, where you can start the steaks over high heat and then finish them on medium. On gas grills with three or more burners,

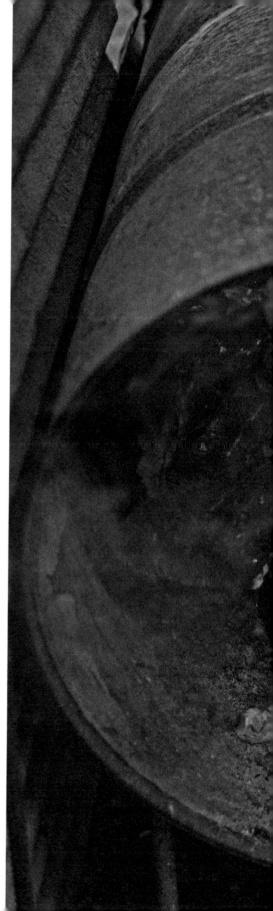

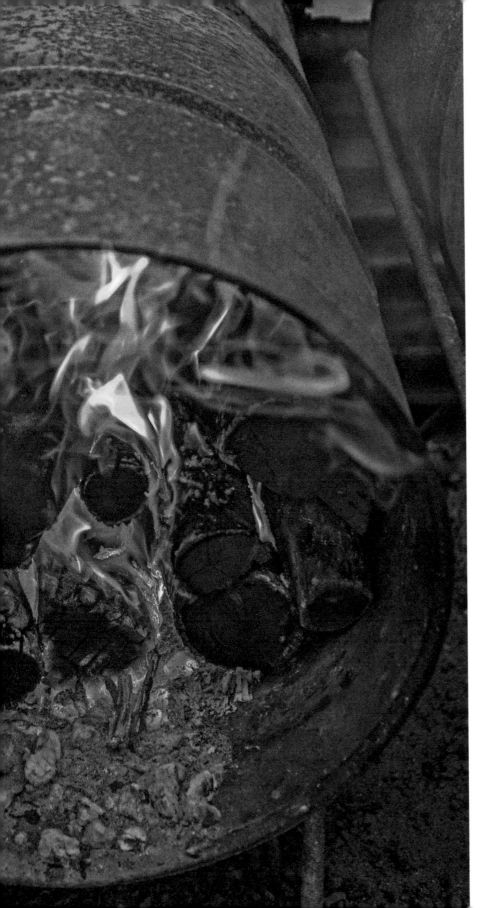

you can usually keep a hot fire and a medium fire going simultaneously from the beginning. On smaller grills, start hot and then turn down the heat at the appropriate point. On charcoal and wood-burning grills, establish two different cooking areas, one with coals in a single layer for moderate heat and another with coals piled two to three layers deep for a hot fire. An infrared burner, common on many high-end grills today, pumps out blazingly high heat for the first stage of cooking. Then grilling can be finished over medium heat on one of the grill's conventional burners.

THE HAND TEST

Our grilling recipes all recommend the "hand test" for gauging the heat of the fire, whether it be from gas, wood, or charcoal. While it might sound a little primitive for our technological age, it really does provide a more accurate measurement of heat than any modern gadget made for the grill. The thermometers built into today's grill hoods register only the oven heat when the cover is closed, not the true grilling temperature. In open grilling, the gauges don't measure a darned thing. The temperature knobs on your gas grills marked hot, medium, and low may provide more help over time, but not until you've determined how the settings compare with your hand measurements.

To test the temperature by hand, place your hand a couple of inches above the cooking grate and count the number of seconds before the heat of the fire forces you to pull your hand away. One to two seconds signifies hot, perfect to start those steaks. Four to five seconds is medium, the level you want to finish the steaks.

Oven-Roasted Beef Tenderloin

STEAK RUB

3 tablespoons kosher salt

1¾ teaspoons coarsely ground black pepper

½ teaspoon granulated garlic

½ teaspoon ground dried oregano

¼ teaspoon granulated onion

¼ teaspoon beef bouillon powder

Pinch of ground white pepper

One 2½-pound beef tenderloin, silverskin and surface fat removed

Olive oil

W hen you want luscious beef for a dinner party but have limited time, or don't want to bother firing up the grill, here's the tenderloin for you. Our signature dry spice rub for steaks helps form a crust on the tenderloin and boosts the buttery meat's flavor without masking it.

Should you be lucky enough to have any leftovers, check out the ideas that follow. When you want a simple appetizer to pass or for people to assemble themselves, each is a top choice, whether using this roasted tenderloin or a Mesquite Smoked Peppered Beef Tenderloin shipped from periniranch.com.

Preheat the oven to 475°F.

Combine all the rub ingredients in a small bowl. Brush the tenderloin lightly with a couple of teaspoons olive oil. Completely coat the tenderloin with all of the rub, pushing it into every little nook

Rub a roasting rack with a teaspoon of oil so the meat and rub won't stick to it. Arrange the tenderloin on the rack and place in the roasting pan.

Insert a meat thermometer into the thickest part of the tenderloin.

Plan on a total roasting time of 30 to 35 minutes. Place the tenderloin in the oven and cook for 10 minutes. Reduce the heat to 425°F and continue roasting for 20 to 25 minutes, until the thermometer reads 130°F (medium-rare). Transfer the meat to a cutting board and let it sit for 10 minutes before slicing.

TENDERLOIN SLIDERS (at left): On each slider bun, arrange a slice or two of tenderloin, drizzle with horseradish sauce (1 cup sour cream mixed with 2 tablespoons prepared horseradish), and sprinkle with chopped parsley.

BEEF TENDERLOIN AND GUACAMOLE CROSTINI: Start with small slices of toasted or grilled sourdough bread. Top each with a sliver of tenderloin, followed by a spoonful of Guacamole (page 23) and a sprinkle of crumbled queso fresco and chopped green onion.

TENDERLOIN-ARUGULA WRAPS: For each, wrap a slice of tenderloin around a few arugula leaves, leaving a tuft of the leaves sticking out of one end. Use a toothpick to hold it together. Serve with Blue Cheese Dressing (page 58) for dipping.

TENDERLOIN-REMOULADE CROSTINI: Spread some Remoulade (page 114) on crostini. Add a slice of tenderloin to each one, followed by a dot of remoulade. Garnish with some capers or lemon zest.

TENDERLOIN BAO BUNS: Steam some frozen Chinese buns, then fill each with a couple of thin slices of tenderloin, a brush of hoisin sauce, and maybe a squirt of sriracha or other Asian chile paste. Tuck in a few cilantro leaves too, if you like.

TENDERLOIN BITES: Using decorative toothpicks, skewer a slice of tenderloin (folded in thirds or quarters), a cherry tomato, and a pepperoncini pepper or a quarter of a seeded jalapeño.

TENDERLOIN-POTATO SKEWERS: Make tiny skewers with a slice of tenderloin (folded in thirds or quarters) and steamed small new potatoes. Drizzle with a bit of pesto or serve with a bowl of Buttermilk Ranch Dressing (page 56).

THE MYSTIQUE OF MESQUITE

||||||||||||||||||||||||||||||

At the Steakhouse, we use mesquite because it's a native Texas tree that grows all around us. Originally, we gathered the wood at the ranch and even chopped it ourselves. Now we go through so much of it that we have it delivered twenty cords at a time. It has to be very dry. Some of our mesquite has been aged for ten years or more, so that the tar and pitch are long gone. It's an excellent high-heat wood for grilling and gives off a fragrant woodsy aroma you immediately associate with the West. To smoke or barbecue with it, you want to burn it down to coals before you start, otherwise the smoke can get acrid over the long time needed to cook, say, a brisket. Foodways Texas and Texas A&M University host an annual Camp Brisket for passionate barbecue fans. Participants learn every detail about cooking the challenging beef cut, including the best woods to use. Each year, there's a side-by-side tasting of brisket cooked over various woods. Mesquite is always at or near the top in the blind taste testing.

OUR MOST MEMORABLE CATERING JOB

||||||||||||||||||||||||||||||||||||||||||||||||||||||||||||||||||||||||||||

When Governor George W. Bush was inaugurated as President Bush "43" in 2001, we dreamed that someday we might have the opportunity to cater an event at the White House. We got The Call later that spring, requesting a Texas-sized and Texas-themed bash for the annual Congressional Picnic in September. We were asked to haul chuck wagons, handcrafted barbecue pits, a trailer full of mesquite, a crew of cowboys, and anything else needed to create an authentic Lone Star feast on the South Lawn of the White House. Austin-based Ray Benson and his band Asleep at the Wheel would be entertaining the 1,400 expected guests, which included all members of the House and Senate and their families. In June, we made a trip to D.C. to work out the details and logistics with the White House chefs and staff. We told them we planned to serve bread pudding, green chile hominy, Southern green beans cooked with bacon drippings, and Mesquite Smoked Peppered Beef Tenderloin. The executive chef looked incredulous, and finally he blurted out that we would *have* to serve chicken. "You're in Washington!" That sucked the air right out of the room. Tom countered with, "When you're serving a Texas chuck wagon meal, you serve beef. If you want another main course, I'll do catfish." It took a consultation with the First Lady, but the menu was approved with all our suggested dishes, plus fried catfish.

We arrived in Washington for the long-planned event on Sunday, September 9. Early the next day we began working with the staff on the food preparation and setting up all the equipment, which included 160 picnic tables. We were up early on the morning of September 11, ready for the big day. While Lisa was still getting dressed, Tom sat down to watch some TV to calm his

nerves. What he saw in no way calmed his nerves; in fact, it was downright horrifying. It was the planes flying into the World Trade Center's twin towers in New York. Looking out the hotel window at the sparkling blue-sky fall day made it all the more incomprehensible. We opened the window and immediately smelled smoke. It was coming from the Pentagon, where another plane had crashed.

Later in the day, a call came from the White House about whether we could give the food for the cancelled party to the firefighters and other first responders. Of course. Then we offered to come over and start the BBQ pits, but it was pointed out that smoke coming from the White House lawn might cause further panic, and that we certainly couldn't do anything that would look festive, so the food was prepared indoors by the White House kitchen staff.

The following day, we were back outside the White House, packing up everything that had been set up on Monday. Tom heard a whistle and his name called out and looked up to see President Bush striding toward him. Now, there's a protocol that you never approach the president; it makes those Secret Service folks real nervous. But we walked up to the commander-in-chief, who, in the midst of the country's biggest crisis, commented that he was sorry we had not been able to cater the party. He also said we'd plan it again because he wasn't going to let terrorists change the way we live our lives. As the president

headed back inside, one of our cowboys hollered out, "We'll be praying for you, Mr. President." He stopped and turned around and said, "Thank you. I need that." And then the most powerful man in the world slipped back into his office to deal with our new reality. True to his promise, we were back at the White House the following year when the tradition of the Congressional Picnic resumed.

Ranch Roasted Prime Rib

PRIME RIB RUB

½ cup coarsely ground black pepper

¼ cup kosher salt

1 tablespoon plus 1 teaspoon garlic powder

1 tablespoon plus 1 teaspoon crumbled dried oregano

One 4-rib rib roast (prime rib), about 8 pounds, bones removed

Logs to fuel a wood-burning smoker, mesquite if available

For a special occasion, few cuts of beef are more visually striking than a prime rib roast. You ought to see it when we lay out forty of them side-by-side for big parties! At the Perini Ranch, we actually have enough barbecue pits to smoke-roast prime rib for 1,200 lucky folks. When our crew slices the beef, it further wows diners because each slice covers most of a plate. It's worth noting that "prime rib" is the full rack from which ribeye steaks are cut. When cut into individual steaks, you get more crustiness in proportion to the meat because a steak is grilled on both sides, but a large prime rib is going to brown just on the outer edges. Both can be delicious. It's a personal preference. We like more pepper in our prime rib rub because, with its higher fat content and larger surface area, the prime rib can handle a more piquant rub.

Combine all the rub ingredients in a small bowl and mix well. Place the roast on a baking sheet. Massage the dry rub all over the roast, really packing it on. Let sit at room temperature while getting the smoker ready.

Fire up the smoker, bringing the temperature to 300°F to 325°F. Logs should be burned down to large coals before adding them to the fire. You will want to do this in some kind of fireproof barrel or tub. Add more coals as needed throughout the hours of smoking to maintain the proper temperature.

Before cooking, take the internal temperature of the meat, deep in the roast's center, with an instant-read thermometer. The temperature should be nearing 40°F, considered the high end of the safe range for beef to sit out unrefrigerated. If the temperature of the roast is more than a couple of degrees below 40°F, plan to extend the cooking time by a few minutes.

Transfer the prime rib to the smoker, fattier side up. Plan on a total cooking time of 2 to 2½ hours. After 1½ hours, check the internal temperature, deep in the roast's center again, to gauge the rest of the cooking time. You don't want to overcook a piece of meat this special. We prefer to take the roast off when it is in the rare to medium-rare range, 120°F to 130°F. We don't advise cooking it beyond 140°F, the high side of medium. (Although you might want to cook the roast just to 140°F, so that you have prime rib of varying doneness.)

Tent the roast loosely with aluminum foil and let sit for 30 minutes. Allowing the roast to rest is essential, so all the meat's juices settle and aren't lost when the roast is sliced. Carve into thick slices and serve.

COLD PRIME RIB ON TOASTED SOURDOUGH WITH HORSERADISH SAUCE: For each sandwich, toast two thin slices of sourdough bread. Lay out one piece of toast and slather one side with horseradish sauce (1 cup sour cream mixed with 2 tablespoons prepared horseradish). Arrange a slice of cold prime rib over the sauce. Add a couple of red-ripe tomato slices and crisp romaine leaves or other lettuce. Top with the remaining slice of toast, smeared with a little more horseradish sauce if you're as crazy for horseradish as we are. Such good eating.

OPEN-FACED HOT PRIME RIB SANDWICHES WITH MELTED CHEDDAR, GRILLED MUSHROOMS, AND ONIONS: Toss thick slices of button mushrooms with thin slices of onion and enough melted butter or vegetable oil to coat them. Grill the vegetables over medium heat or sauté in a medium skillet until tender. Arrange one slice of white bread per person on a baking sheet. Top each one with a slice of prime rib. Spoon on the mushrooms and onion slices. Top with 2 slices medium or sharp Cheddar. Bake at 450°F for 3 to 5 minutes, until the cheese is melting and gooey.

West Texas Mesquite Smoked Brisket

SERVES 12 TO 15

One 8- to 12-pound packer-trimmed beef brisket

BRISKET RUB

¼ cup plus 2 tablespoons coarse ground black pepper

¼ cup chili powder

¼ cup kosher salt

2 tablespoons garlic powder

2 tablespoons onion powder

BRISKET MOP

1½ cups vegetable oil or rendered beef tallow

1½ cups white vinegar

½ medium red onion, cut into 4 pieces

2 medium lemons, halved

Logs to fuel a wood-burning smoker, mesquite if available

We cook our wildly popular smoked briskets for special events and catered parties. You can mail order it any time of the year from periniranch.com, but here's our technique if you'd like to make it for yourself. It takes about 12 hours—about as long as it takes to drink two 6-packs of beer, according to our crew—to smoke a full "packer-trimmed" brisket, the style that includes both the point and flat cuts.

I'd like to give credit here to my friend Cliff Teinert, from Albany, Texas. In the 1970s, we cooked together a lot and it's from Cliff that I learned about correctly making coals and cooking on pits, especially when it comes to brisket. We cook them West Texas style, which involves burning mesquite logs down to coals, and then cooking the meat low and slow at a temperature of 250°F to 275°F. While the briskets are cooking, we "mop" them with a mixture of oil or rendered beef fat, vinegar, and some seasonings, which keeps the meat moist and adds a layer of flavor. We strive for a good hit of smokiness from the fire, but not so much smoke that it masks the brisket's classic beefiness. We leave off any accompanying sauce for the same reason. Depending on your smoker and the size of your crowd, you might want to do a second brisket at the same time. It's not unusual for us to smoke some fifty briskets at a time. If you don't have a smoker or barbecue pit of some kind, or a heavy-duty grill, try the oven variation.

Trim the brisket of any large pieces of fat or membrane. Turn so the fat-covered side is up. Trim the surface fat to an even ¼ to ½ inch. Cut out any visible pieces of hard fat where the point and flat portions of the brisket meet. Place the brisket on a baking sheet.

TO MAKE THE RUB: Combine all the rub ingredients in a small bowl.

Apply the rub evenly to the brisket, massaging it into every crevice. Let the brisket sit on a baking sheet at room temperature for up to an hour while preparing the smoker.

Fire up the smoker, bringing the temperature to 250°F to 275°F. Logs should be burned down to large coals before adding them to the fire. You will want to do this in some kind of fireproof barrel or tub. Add more coals as needed throughout the hours of smoking to maintain the proper temperature.

TO MAKE THE MOP: Combine 1½ cups hot water, oil, vinegar, onion, and lemon halves in a medium saucepan over low heat and heat until warmed.

Put the brisket, fat-side up, directly on the smoker grate. Cook the brisket until well done and very tender, 1 to 1¼ hours per pound. An 8-pound brisket will take

9 to 10 hours, while a 12-pound one will require at least 12 hours. Once an hour, baste the brisket with the mop and turn it. Keep the mop warm. If it begins to run low, add more hot water or make another batch. When the brisket is cooked, it should have a dark crust, almost like black bark, and its internal temperature should read 190°F to 200°F on an instant-read thermometer.

Once the brisket is cooked, transfer it from the smoker to a platter. If you are planning to serve the meat within 30 to 45 minutes, let it sit at room temperature. If it will be longer, wrap the meat in a couple of layers of uncoated butcher or parchment paper. (Don't use aluminum foil; it will steam the meat and soften the desirable crust.)

Slice the meat thinly against the grain, down through both the fattier point and leaner flat cut portions of meat. Watch as you work, though, because the grain changes directions. Serve immediately.

OVEN-ROASTED BRISKET: While this version lacks the serious crustiness achieved in a smoker over some dozen hours, the coarsely ground pepper adds a lot of character. If you use a smoked pepper, such as Whiskey Barrel Smoked Black Pepper from savoryspice.com, you'll add another delicious layer of flavor. Start with a 4-pound brisket flat cut. Put the brisket in a roasting pan. Make just half of the rub and massage it into the brisket. Bake uncovered for 1 hour at 350°F. Pour 1½ cups beef stock around the brisket and add water as needed to equal about ½ inch of liquid in the pan. Cover the pan tightly. Reduce the temperature to 325°F and continue baking for about 3 more hours, until fork-tender.

Chicken-Fried Steak with Cream Gravy

SERVES 4

1¾ to 2 pounds boneless ribeye steak, cut into 4 equal portions, trimmed of all sinew and fat

¾ cup whole milk

1 large egg, beaten

2 teaspoons salt

½ teaspoon freshly ground black pepper

2 cups all-purpose flour

Vegetable oil or shortening, for frying

CREAM GRAVY

3 tablespoons all-purpose flour

2 cups cold whole milk

Kosher salt and freshly ground black pepper

We can't overstate the importance of chicken-fried steak to Texas culture. In 2011, October 26 was proclaimed Texas Chicken Fried Steak Day by the state legislature. It's a holiday on our calendar and we serve tons of CFS to honor the day. The dish has been handed down from the 19th-century heyday of cattle drives and cowboys. Cattle drives aren't such a big deal today, but we get plenty of Texas folks who think nothing of driving several hours for a great meal. In fact, people come from all across Texas and beyond to enjoy this golden-fried, crusty slab of steak, which is served only at our Sunday buffet, and of course, on October 26. Most restaurants and recipes use round steak (a rear-end cut with little marbling), but at the Steakhouse, we prefer boneless ribeyes for our "chicken-fried."

Both of us, at separate times, have been president of the Texas Restaurant Association, the only husband-and-wife team to have held that honor. One of the handy statistics that the association came up with is that some 90 percent of Texas restaurants serve chicken-fried steak. We're not sure that even 90 percent would say they serve coffee. You'll want some Mashed Potatoes (page 138) along with this to sop up the cream gravy, which also goes well generously spooned over Buttermilk Biscuits (page 148) and The Judge's Fried Chicken (page 106).

Using a meat mallet, pound the steak pieces ¼-inch thick. Whisk together the milk, egg, salt, and pepper in a shallow plate. Spread the flour on another shallow dish. One at a time, dredge the steak pieces in the egg-milk mixture, then in the flour. Repeat dredging in the liquid and then the flour. The surface of the meat should be fairly dry.

Clip a deep-fry thermometer to the inside of a deep 12- or 14-inch cast-iron skillet or Dutch oven. Pour in oil to a depth of 1 inch and bring the temperature of the oil to 325°F over medium-high heat. Line a baking sheet with paper towels. Put a wire baking rack on top of the paper towels.

When the oil is hot, add the steaks, in batches if necessary. In 4 to 5 minutes, when the meat juices start to pool on top of each piece and the bottoms are golden brown, turn the steaks and cook until golden brown, 4 to 5 minutes more. Drain the steaks on the rack and transfer to a warm platter. Keep them warm while you prepare the gravy.

TO MAKE THE GRAVY:
Pour off the fat from the pan through a strainer, leaving ¼ cup fat and pan drippings in the bottom of the skillet, discarding the rest. Return any browned cracklings in the strainer to the skillet. Warm the pan drippings over medium heat. Add the flour, whisking to avoid lumps. Add the milk, whisking frequently, bring to a simmer, and cook until the gravy is thickened, about 3 minutes. Stir the gravy up from the bottom frequently, scraping up the browned bits. Add salt and a good amount of pepper so the cream gravy has more than a suspicion of pepper. Taste for seasoning. Pour the gravy over the steaks or on the side and serve immediately.

Texas Chili

Back in 1977, our Texas legislature saw fit to make chili the state dish. There was, however, precious little agreement on the ingredients and best recipe. The only thing all Texans can assent to is that Texas chili does *not* include beans. Be sure, though, to include some of our state pepper, the jalapeño; and, if you wish, cook it in our official state cooking implement, the cast-iron Dutch oven.

"Chili-grind" beef is a good bit coarser than meat ground for burgers. It's ground daily that way in many Texas markets, and can usually be requested anywhere that has a meat department. It's very important to get the right texture for the chili. Accompany each serving with a wedge of Skillet Cornbread (page 155) or Cheddar-Jalapeño Cornbread (page 156).

SERVES 8 OR MORE

4 pounds chili-grind beef with 20% fat content

1 large onion, diced

1 tablespoon minced garlic

3 tablespoons chili powder

1 tablespoon ground cumin

1 teaspoon crumbled dried oregano

1 cup Pace Picante Sauce, preferably medium heat

1 cup diced tomatoes (about 1 large), or 1 cup canned diced tomatoes with juice

Kosher salt

Freshly ground black pepper

1 jalapeño, minced

Combine the beef, onion, and garlic in a large Dutch oven and cook over medium-high heat, stirring frequently, until evenly browned. Stir in the chili powder, cumin, oregano, picante sauce, tomatoes and juice, and 2 cups hot water. Bring to a boil over medium-high heat. Reduce the heat to a simmer, cover, and cook for 1 hour, stirring frequently, until the chili thickens.

Add at least 1 teaspoon salt, a few grinds of pepper, and the jalapeño and cook for 15 minutes. Taste again and if needed, add a bit more salt or pepper, and cook for another few minutes.

Serve piping hot in bowls. The chili can be cooled, covered, and refrigerated overnight, and reheated or frozen.

BISON CHILI: Use 3 pounds coarsely ground bison and 1 pound ground beef. The beef is fattier than the bison and gives bison chili a richer mouthfeel.

TOM'S TEXAS CHILI TOUR

||||||||||||||||||||||

For about eight years, Tom served as the national spokesperson for Pace Picante Sauce. He knew the Pace family in San Antonio going back to the early 1960s and his time at Peacock Military Academy. From 1996 to 2003, Tom traveled coast-to-coast sharing his knowledge of chuck wagon history and Texas food. Tom developed this Texas chili recipe for the tour using Pace Picante Sauce.

Beef Fajitas

SERVES 6

Two 1- to 1¼-pound skirt steaks, trimmed of membranes and excess fat

1 tablespoon kosher salt

1 tablespoon coarsely ground black pepper

Guacamole (page 23)

Pico de Gallo (page 22) or other salsa

Shredded Cheddar or Monterey Jack

1 dozen flour tortillas, warmed

It's hard to imagine that grilled skirt steak wrapped in tortillas was little known beyond the Rio Grande Valley's *vaqueros,* or cowboys, until the 1970s. That's when Texas restaurants and food booths at fairs and festivals caught on and fajitas became popular; they've been on our catering menu since the Steakhouse opened in 1983.

Folks sometimes prepare fajitas with flank steak or even sirloin, but we prefer the classic long, flat, and beefy skirt steak. While all steaks should be sliced against, not with, the grain, it's essential to do so with skirt steak, or the slices will be tough and stringy rather than tender. Ask your butcher for "inside" skirt; it's a little more tender and will cost a bit more, but it's worth it.

Cut each steak in half to make two shorter, more manageable pieces of the meat. Combine the salt and pepper and rub them into the meat. Let the steaks sit uncovered at room temperature while preparing the grill.

Fire up the grill for a two-level fire capable of cooking on high (1 to 2 seconds with the hand test—see page 81) and medium heat (4 to 5 seconds with the hand test) at the same time. If grilling over gas or charcoal, add a half-dozen mesquite chunks to the fire shortly before placing the steaks on the grill.

Grill the steaks over high heat for 3 to 4 minutes per side if less than ½ inch thick, or 4 to 5 minutes per side if more than ½ inch thick, until medium-rare. Turn the steaks more often if juice pools on the surface. Tent with aluminum foil and let rest for 5 minutes.

Holding a knife at a slight diagonal, slice the steaks across the grain into thin finger-length strips.

To serve, pile the steak strips on a platter, accompanied by bowls of guacamole, salsa, and shredded cheese, and a napkin-lined basket of warm tortillas.

The TODAY Show Award-Winning Ranch Burgers

SERVES 6

STEAK RUB

3 tablespoons kosher salt

1¾ teaspoons coarsely ground black pepper

½ teaspoon granulated garlic

½ teaspoon ground dried oregano

¼ teaspoon granulated onion

¼ teaspoon beef bouillon powder

Pinch of ground white pepper

BURGERS

3 pounds freshly ground chuck with 20% fat content

Vegetable oil (if cooking in a skillet)

6 sturdy burger buns, halved

6 slices medium Cheddar or provolone, at room temperature

4 ounces thinly sliced button mushrooms, grilled or sautéed

¾ to 1 cup chopped fresh-roasted or jarred New Mexican green chiles

Mustard or mayonnaise, tomato slices, iceberg lettuce leaves, grilled thin onion slices, pickle slices

A dozen or so years ago, we decided our burger needed an upgrade. We dissected every element of it, from bun to burger to condiments. We experimented cooking burgers on a griddle vs. a grill. We cooked them at different temperatures. We finally built our perfect burger, and it wasn't long after that *Food Network* magazine proclaimed it to be the best burger in all of Texas. *Texas Monthly* chimed in, elevating the burger to its best burger list as well. The staff of NBC's TODAY show was scouring America's best burger lists to run a competition at Rockefeller Plaza, where the show tapes in New York City. They invited us to compete against other cooks. Most of the other burgers and cooking techniques were way over the top. One was even called Heart Attack on a Plate. We called them "all hat, no cattle." Tom set up a small three-legged grill and cooked what we do best. A Ranch burger with fresh roasted green chiles, grilled mushrooms, onions, and some sliced cheese. The judges chose Tom's no-frills burger as the winner!

A burger is only as good as its parts. Everything counts, from the ground chuck to the cheese to the bun. The bun should have enough firmness to stand up to the meat patty but should also feel soft when lightly pressed. Pass on wimpy buns that fall apart under the heft and the juiciness of the burger. Our slightly sweet sourdough buns come from Sheila Partin's Sweet Mesquite Bakery in Houston. You can order these white sandwich buns online at sbakery.com.

Directions follow for cooking these on a grill or in a cast-iron skillet. No matter which cooking method you choose, avoid mashing the burgers down with a spatula; delicious juices will be lost.

TO MAKE THE RUB: Combine all the ingredients in a large bowl. Add the ground chuck and, using clean hands, mix well.

TO MAKE THE BURGERS: Divide and shape the beef into 6 equal balls. Pat each ball into ¾-inch-thick patties. Handle gently, so that the burgers hold together but are somewhat loose, not firmly packed.

TO GRILL THE BURGERS: Fire up the grill for a two-level fire capable of cooking first on high heat (1 to 2 seconds with the hand test—see page 81) and then on medium heat (4 to 5 seconds with the hand test).

For best flavor if cooking over gas or charcoal, add a half-dozen mesquite chunks to the fire a few minutes before putting the burgers on the grill.

Grill the burgers over high heat for 1½ minutes per side. Move the burgers to medium heat and rotate a half-turn for grill marks. Cook for an additional 3½ to 4 minutes per side, until crusty on the outside and with a bare hint of pink at the center for medium, or more or less to desired doneness.

Place the bottom of a bun on a plate. Arrange a cheeseburger patty on top of the bun. Spoon on the mushrooms and green chiles. Place the bun top and all the other condiments on the side and serve.

TO COOK THE BURGERS IN A SKILLET: Heat a large cast-iron skillet over high heat. Add just enough oil to coat the bottom of the skillet. Turn the heat down to medium and rotate skillet around to distribute the oil. Add three of the burgers, if they fit without crowding. Cook for 3 minutes and turn once. Place a slice of cheese on top of each burger and cook until medium-rare, about 3 minutes longer. Cook the second batch of burgers.

PORK
BISON
LAMB
CHICKEN
SEAFOOD

Mesquite Smoked Pork Ribs

SERVES 4 TO 6

RIB RUB

2 tablespoons coarse-ground black pepper

2 tablespoons sweet paprika

1 tablespoon kosher salt

1½ teaspoons dry mustard

1½ teaspoons garlic powder

¾ teaspoon cayenne

Two 2-pound slabs pork back ribs or St. Louis cut spareribs (trimmed of chine bones and brisket flap), preferably from a heritage pork breed, such as Duroc or Berkshire

Logs to fuel a wood-burning smoker, mesquite if available

At Perini Ranch Steakhouse, we're all about beef, but pork ribs have always been popular on the Texas barbecue scene. Our ribs are rubbed with spices and smoked, then served without sauce. Look for Duroc, Berkshire, or other well-marbled heritage pork ribs. Use either back or spareribs. With spareribs, ask your butcher to cut them St. Louis style, which removes a cartilage-loaded portion of the sternum and an odd tough bit of flap meat. The cut also squares up the rack, making it easier to cook, slice, and eat. We burn down mesquite logs, and then cook the ribs directly over smoking white-hot coals at 250°F for 3 to 3½ hours.

To oven-bake the ribs, see the instructions at the end of the recipe.

Combine all the rub ingredients in a small bowl. Massage both sides of the rib racks with the rub. Let the ribs sit at room temperature for 30 minutes.

Fire up a smoker, bringing its temperature to 225°F to 250°F. Logs should be burned down to large coals in some kind of fireproof barrel or tub before adding them to the fire. Add more coals as needed throughout the hours of smoking to maintain the proper temperature.

Transfer the ribs to the smoker, meaty sides up, and cook for 3 hours. Turn the rib racks over and cook for another 30 minutes. They are ready when you pick up a rack from the center with tongs and it relaxes and droops. The meat should pull easily from the bones but be short of falling off. Cut the ribs parallel to the bones into individual pieces. Serve immediately with plenty of napkins.

OVEN-BAKED SPARE RIBS Heat the oven to 225°F. Rub the ribs with the dry rub as described above. As with the oven-baked brisket, using a smoked pepper will add a good hit of extra flavor. Place the ribs close together on a baking sheet lined with a silicone mat. Cover the baking sheet with foil and bake for 2½ hours. Uncover and bake for about 1 hour longer. They are ready when you pick up a rack from the center with tongs and it relaxes and droops. The meat should pull easily from the bones but be short of falling off.

HEAD OF THE CLASS

IIIIIIIIIIIIIIIIIIIIIIIIIIIIIIIIIIIIIIII

Back in 1989, Tom's friend Watt Matthews wanted to hold a special party for his Princeton class reunion. He asked us to fix a pit-roasted steer's head, an old South Texas barbecue specialty called *barbacoa*. Well sure, we said, we can do that! The only problem was that we had never seen one, much less cooked one. Since the request was made well before you could easily find information on the Internet, the only reference we could come up with was from the epic Texas movie, *Giant.* In the 1956 film, Leslie Lynnton Benedict, Elizabeth Taylor's character, fainted at the sight of the cooked steer's head, which perhaps should have been a harbinger to us of things to come.

We dug a hefty hole in the ground for the pit/oven, built a wood fire, and cooked the canvas-wrapped steer head on the hot coals for 18 hours. When it was time to pull it out, all these Princeton-educated CEOs were watching with great excitement and curiosity. We acted like we haul cow heads out of pits every day. With great fanfare, we dug up the thing, then unwrapped it and plopped it on a table. As Tom remembered from the movie, we broke it open with a hatchet and served it straight out of the skull. People lined up and we offered them pit-cooked meat from the head and scoops of the brains. We smiled and carried on as if this was utterly normal for us. One of the wives reacted—almost—in Liz Taylor style. She didn't end up fainting, but she just couldn't deal with it. After apologizing, she headed over to the calf fries and put a great big helping on her plate. No one had the heart to tell her what she was enjoying.

Pulled Pork

SERVES 12 OR MORE

PULLED PORK RUB

½ **cup kosher salt**

½ **cup freshly ground black pepper**

¼ **cup dry mustard**

One 12- to 14-pound pork butt (sometimes called Boston butt), fat cap trimmed off

Logs to fuel a wood-burning smoker, mesquite if available

L isa's brother, Tom Sanders, fine-tuned this version of South Carolina-style pork butt, one of the dishes that has secured him the reputation as the ultimate tailgater in support of the family's beloved Clemson Tigers. Tom Perini has learned to love all of the Sanders' family food favorites, from boiled peanuts to shrimp and grits, but pulled pork was perhaps the easiest for him to embrace. We make this for catered events, turning it into sandwiches with a topping of some coleslaw and a mustard-based barbecue sauce. We smoke the pork butt over mesquite coals, but brother Tom uses a combination of pecan and cherry woods.

TO MAKE THE RUB: Combine all of the ingredients in a small bowl. Apply the rub evenly to the pork butt, massaging it into every crevice. Let the pork butt sit on a baking sheet at room temperature for up to an hour while preparing the smoker.

Fire up the smoker, bringing the temperature to 250°F to 275°F. Logs should be burned down to large coals before adding them to the fire. Do this in a fireproof barrel or tub. Add more coals as needed throughout the hours of smoking to maintain the proper temperature.

If cooking over gas or charcoal, add 6 large chunks of wood to the fire, shortly before transferring the pork butt to the smoker.

Put the pork butt directly on the smoker grate. Cook the pork butt until well done and very tender. When done, the pork butt will have a dark crust, almost like black bark, be pull-apart tender, and its internal temperature should read 190°F on an instant-read thermometer.

Remove the pork from the smoker to a platter and let it sit until cool enough to handle, about 15 minutes. Pull off chunks of the meat, then shred them. Make sure each serving has some of the darker chewier meat along with some of the lighter interior meat.

Braised Bison Short Ribs

SERVES 4 TO 6

4 pounds meaty bone-in English-cut bison or beef short ribs

2 medium tomatoes, halved through their equators

2 jalapeños, halved lengthwise

1 large onion, quartered

8 ounces button mushrooms, halved if large

3 green onions, chopped

1 cup plus ½ cup dry red wine, such as Cabernet Sauvignon or Merlot

4 cups low-sodium beef stock

⅓ cup Worcestershire sauce

1 bay leaf

1 tablespoon onion powder

1½ teaspoons kosher salt, or more to taste

½ teaspoon granulated garlic

½ teaspoon ground white pepper

½ teaspoon dried crumbled oregano

¼ teaspoon whole black peppercorns

¼ cup cornstarch

Buffalo once did roam through Buffalo Gap, coming to drink at nearby Elm Creek. We created this hearty dish for the Comanche Moon Social, an annual local fundraiser for the Taylor County History Center, where Tom serves on the board. A Comanche moon refers to the bright full moon that warriors preferred for their fearsome raids. Bison ribs are leaner and more expensive than readily available beef ribs; either will work here, although beef ribs are more sizeable so you may need to add about 30 minutes to the baking time. We like short ribs with a side of Mashed Potatoes (page 138) and some crusty bread.

Heat the oven to 325°F.

Place the short ribs, tomatoes, jalapeños, onion, mushrooms, and green onions in a Dutch oven or stockpot. Add 1 cup of the wine, the stock, Worcestershire, bay leaf, onion powder, salt, garlic, white pepper, oregano, and peppercorns. Bring to a simmer over high heat, cover, and transfer to the oven. Bake for 2 to 2½ hours, until the meat is pull-apart tender when pierced with a fork.

Using tongs, transfer the ribs to a platter and cover with aluminum foil. Strain the cooking liquid through a large fine-mesh strainer into a large saucepan. Using the back of a wooden spoon, press down on the vegetables to get every bit of flavor and juice from them. Discard the vegetables in the strainer.

Bring the cooking liquid to a boil over medium-high heat. Lower the heat and simmer to reduce the sauce by about one-third, 10 to 15 minutes. Whisk together the remaining ½ cup wine and the cornstarch in a bowl so there are no lumps. Stir the wine-cornstarch mixture into the sauce. Continue cooking until the sauce thickens, 2 to 3 minutes longer.

While the sauce is reducing, use two forks to pull the meat from the bones. Discard the bones and cartilage. Add the meat to the sauce, heat through, and serve.

OUR FOUR-LEGGED AMBASSADORS

||||||||||||||||||||||||||||||||

When you think of a ranch dog, the basset hound—with its short legs, long ears, and an even longer body—probably doesn't come to mind. Lisa brought the first basset hound into our lives. That's Gus, who has even written his own book, *Tails of Perini Ranch,* about all the cool things to do around the property. Gus was lucky enough to have Miss Beazley, a former White House dog, pen the foreword to his book. Miss Beazley noted that she had dictated her words to a member of *her* staff, Laura Bush, and to please excuse any typos that Mrs. Bush might have made.

Gus was named after Captain Augustus "Gus" McCrae, a character from Larry McMurtry's seminal western novel, *Lonesome Dove.* Our friend Robert Duvall played Gus in the memorable TV mini-series. Gus now has a younger brother, Jett, whose namesake, Jett Rink, was the character James Dean played in the movie *Giant.* Gus and Jett check out the ranch with Tom, riding in his "mule," a four-wheeled heavy-duty open-sided vehicle. Daily at 8:00 a.m., Tom, Gus, and Jett load up in the mule and head to the Steakhouse for coffee and the morning meeting to plan the day.

Grilled Lamb Rib Chops with Jalapeño Jelly

SERVES 6

LAMB CHOP RUB

1 tablespoon kosher salt

½ teaspoon coarsely ground black pepper

¼ teaspoon granulated garlic

¼ teaspoon ground dried oregano

6 single-cut frenched lamb chops

Jalapeño jelly, warmed

Combine all the rub ingredients in a small bowl. Massage each chop generously with the dry rub. Let the chops sit at room temperature for 30 minutes.

Fire up the grill for a two-level fire capable of cooking first on high heat (1 to 2 seconds with the hand test—see page 81) and then on medium (4 to 5 seconds with the hand test). For the best flavor if cooking over gas or charcoal, add a half-dozen mesquite chunks to the fire shortly before placing the chops on the grill.

Grill the chops over high heat for 1½ to 2 minutes per side. Move the chops to medium heat, turning them again, and continue grilling for 2 to 2½ minutes per side for medium-rare. Serve immediately, with a side of jelly.

Frenched lamb chops are cleaned of fat on the rib bones, making them easy to pick up and eat with your fingers. We cover them with steak rub and, once nicely charred, serve with jalapeño jelly. We prefer to buy lamb that hasn't been shipped frozen from the other side of the world, since there's plenty of delicious meat available from American ranchers.

The Judge's Fried Chicken

SERVES 4 TO 6

EGG WASH

1 large egg

¾ cup whole or 2% milk

2 teaspoons salt

1 teaspoon kosher salt

½ teaspoon freshly ground black pepper

½ teaspoon ground white pepper

2 cups all-purpose flour

One 3½- to 4-pound chicken, cut into 9 bone-in serving pieces

Vegetable oil for pan-frying

Back in 1878, the small settlement of Buffalo Gap was designated the Taylor County seat to honor three local Taylor brothers who fought at the Alamo. When the railroad was built in the 1880s, it bypassed Buffalo Gap and a new city, to be called Abilene after the Kansas cattle town, was planned along the train route. As Abilene grew into a shipping center, its citizens began to agitate to become the county seat. Two judges, one from each town, were to sort out the governmental matter. The Buffalo Gap judge ended up throwing his support behind Abilene. In retaliation, the local denizens raided the judge's property, absconded with his many chickens, and cooked up a fine fried chicken dinner. To hear people talk, you'd think this happened fifteen years ago, rather than fifteen decades ago. To honor this uprising, we serve fried chicken at every Sunday buffet.

We cut up whole chickens into nine recognizable pieces: two breasts, two wings, two thighs, two legs, and a pulley bone (or wishbone). At Sunday brunch, we're glad to see folks making wishes over pulley bones!

TO MAKE THE EGG WASH: Whisk the egg in a shallow dish. Add the milk, salt, kosher salt, black pepper, and white pepper and whisk until combined. Put the flour in another shallow bowl. Line a baking sheet with paper towels and set a wire baking rack on top.

Clip a deep-fry thermometer to the inside of a deep 12- or 14-inch cast-iron skillet or Dutch oven. Pour in oil to a depth of 3 inches and bring to 325°F over medium-high heat.

Dip the drumsticks in the egg wash. Hold the drumsticks over the bowl for a few seconds so some of the wash drips away, then dredge in the flour, shaking off any excess. Carefully lower them into the hot oil. Repeat with the wings, then the thighs, and then the breasts and the pulley bone, placing them skin-side down in the oil. Plan on a total frying time of 30 minutes: Fry for 15 minutes, then use tongs to turn each piece, using light pressure to avoid piercing the crust, and fry for an additional 15 to 17 minutes. To check for doneness, insert an instant-read thermometer into the meat of several pieces of chicken without touching the bone. The temperature should be 165°F and the crust should be a rich, golden brown on all sides, with the meat cooked through but still juicy. Drain the chicken on the wire rack. Serve hot.

Crispy Chicken Sandwiches with Chipotle Mayonnaise

MAKES 4 SANDWICHES

CHIPOTLE MAYONNAISE

¾ cup mayonnaise

1½ tablespoons chopped chipotle chiles from a 7-ounce can of chipotle chiles en adobo, with a teaspoon or 2 of the adobo sauce for more heat

Vegetable oil for deep-frying

2 large eggs

¾ cup whole milk

1 teaspoon table salt

1¼ cups all-purpose flour

¼ cup Cajun seasoning

Four 5- to 6-ounce boneless, skinless chicken breasts, pounded to ½-inch thickness

4 soft sandwich rolls

Shredded iceberg or romaine lettuce leaves and red-ripe tomato slices

Jason Mayes has worked in our kitchen for more than two decades. He came up with this fried chicken breast sandwich, which is now on our lunch menu. We like it with a side of sweet-and-spicy bread-and-butter pickles.

TO MAKE THE MAYONNAISE:
Combine the mayonnaise, chiles, and adobo sauce (if you want more heat) in a food processor. Puree until smooth. The mayo will keep for at least a week covered and refrigerated.

Clip a deep-fry thermometer to the inside of a 12-inch cast-iron skillet or Dutch oven. Pour in the oil to a depth of 3 inches and heat to 325°F over medium-high heat. Line a baking sheet with paper towels. Put a wire baking rack on top of the paper towels.

Whisk together the eggs, milk, and salt in a medium bowl. Stir together the flour and Cajun seasoning on a plate. Dunk each chicken breast in the egg wash, letting extra drip back into the bowl, then dredge in the seasoned flour. Dunk again in the egg wash and dredge again in the flour.

Fry the chicken breasts in batches, if necessary, for 12 to 14 minutes, until the chicken is deeply golden-brown and crisp on the outside and white throughout the inside. Make a small nick in one of the pieces to check its doneness. Transfer to the rack to drain.

Dress each sandwich roll generously with chipotle mayonnaise, lay a chicken breast on each, top with shredded lettuce and tomato, and serve right away.

Southern Fried Catfish with Tartar Sauce

SERVES 6

TARTAR SAUCE

1 cup mayonnaise

1 cup finely diced yellow onion

1 cup finely diced dill pickles, squeezed in paper towels to eliminate excess juice

1 tablespoon Worcestershire sauce

1 teaspoon Tabasco sauce

½ teaspoon yellow mustard

½ teaspoon kosher salt, or more to taste

¼ teaspoon freshly ground black pepper

EGG WASH

1 large egg

¾ cup whole or 2% milk

2 teaspoons seasoned salt, such as Lawry's

½ teaspoon freshly ground white pepper

CORNMEAL COATING

2 cups medium-grind yellow cornmeal

¼ cup all-purpose flour

1 teaspoon kosher salt

1 teaspoon cayenne

½ teaspoon freshly ground black pepper

¼ teaspoon onion powder

¼ teaspoon garlic powder

Vegetable oil, for deep-frying

Six 5- to 7-ounce catfish fillets, sliced lengthwise in half if any are larger than others

Because we and many of our customers are cattle ranchers, we don't offer much in the way of pork, seafood, or poultry, which are seen as competitors to the beef industry. The most notable exception is fried catfish, coated in spicy cornmeal and fried to a golden crispness, which is nearly as popular at the Steakhouse and catering events as our steaks. Look for Mississippi farm-raised catfish, which is consistently great and becomes flaky when cooked. Just about any of our sides go with fried catfish.

Credit for our homemade tartar sauce goes to our long-time manager, Dale Cronk, who developed this recipe. Our catfish wouldn't be the same without it. It's chunky, fresh, and one of our most requested recipes.

TO MAKE THE TARTAR SAUCE: Whisk together all the ingredients in a bowl. Cover and refrigerate for up to 2 days, until ready to use.

TO MAKE THE EGG WASH: Whisk together all the ingredients in a shallow bowl.

TO MAKE THE COATING: Stir together all the ingredients in another shallow bowl.

TO COAT AND FRY THE FISH: Clip a deep-fry thermometer to the inside of a deep 12- or 14-inch cast-iron skillet or Dutch oven. Pour in oil to a depth of 3 inches and bring to 325°F over medium-high heat. Line a baking sheet with paper towels. Put a wire baking rack on top of the paper towels.

Dip a catfish strip into the egg wash to coat and hold over the bowl for a few seconds so some of the egg wash drips off. Dredge it in the coating to cover well on all sides. Shake the strip to remove any excess coating, then carefully transfer to the hot oil. Repeat with another 6 strips. To maintain an even temperature, avoid crowding the skillet. Fry the strips for 5 to 6 minutes. When they are golden and float to the surface, place them on the wire rack. Repeat with the remaining strips. Serve hot with the tartar sauce.

Grilled Cajun Catfish

SERVES 4 TO 6

Vegetable oil spray

Six 8- to 10-ounce catfish fillets,
¾ inch thick

3 medium limes, halved through
their equators

2 tablespoons salted butter,
melted

¼ cup Cajun seasoning

Tartar Sauce (page 110),
for serving

An alternative to fried fish,
this version is flaky with some
crispiness to the edges.

Fire up the grill, bringing the temperature to medium-high (3 seconds with
the hand test—see page 81). Spray a
small-mesh grill rack with vegetable
oil spray and place it over the grate.

Just before putting the fillets on the
grill, spray both sides of each with
vegetable oil spray, then spray the cut
sides of each lime wedge. Arrange
the limes around the edges of the
grill. Place the fillets directly over the
heat, drizzle lightly with about half
the butter, and sprinkle evenly with
half the Cajun seasoning. Grill the
fillets uncovered for 3 minutes.
Using a large spatula, carefully turn
them, drizzle again with butter and
sprinkle with the Cajun seasoning,
and cook for about 3 minutes. Carefully turn them once more, rotating
a half-turn, so one side crisps a bit
more than the other, and cook for a
minute or two longer (for a total of
7 to 9 minutes).

Serve the fish immediately with a
charred lime half and tartar sauce.

Dusted Fried Shrimp

SERVES 6

Vegetable oil for deep-frying

2 large eggs

¾ cup whole milk

1 teaspoon table salt

1¼ cups all-purpose flour

¼ cup Cajun seasoning

2½ pounds (16 to 20 per pound) medium-to-large shrimp, shelled, tail-on

The secret to excellent fried shrimp is to keep the coating light and the oil hot (we use the term "dusted" to emphasize that our coating is light). The pink color of the shrimp should show through and you should be able to taste the shrimp as soon as you bite into the crackling, crisp crust. Enjoy with a squeeze of lemon, a favorite cocktail sauce, or perhaps our Remoulade (page 114).

Clip a deep-fry thermometer to the inside of a deep 12- or 14-inch cast-iron skillet or Dutch oven. Pour in oil to a depth of 3 inches and bring to 325°F over medium-high heat. Line a baking sheet with paper towels. Put a wire baking rack on top of the paper towels.

Whisk together the eggs, milk, and salt in a bowl. Combine the flour and Cajun seasoning on a shallow plate. Add the shrimp to the egg mixture, stirring to coat all of them. One by one, dip the shrimp lightly in the flour mixture and shake to eliminate any excess flour. In batches, add the shrimp to the oil and fry until golden brown, about 1½ minutes. Don't crowd the pot or else the temperature of the oil will drop and the shrimp won't be crisp. When cooked, use a slotted spoon or tongs to transfer the shrimp to the wire rack. Repeat with the remaining shrimp. Serve hot.

Seafood Slaw

REMOULADE

1 cup mayonnaise

2 tablespoons Creole mustard

2 tablespoons sweet
pickle relish

1 tablespoon minced
pickled jalapeño

1 tablespoon capers, drained

2 teaspoons minced fresh
flat-leaf parsley leaves

1½ teaspoons
Worcestershire sauce

½ teaspoon prepared
horseradish

½ teaspoon anchovy paste

¼ teaspoon Old Bay seasoning

¼ teaspoon sweet paprika

SLAW

½ medium green cabbage,
shredded

½ medium red cabbage,
shredded

¼ cup salted pepitas
(hulled pumpkin seeds)

1 pound (16 to 20 per pound)
medium-to-large shrimp,
cooked, peeled, deveined, and
halved lengthwise

1 pound cooked lobster meat,
cut into ½-inch pieces

Lisa created this as a cool summer catering entree, and we serve it plated or in martini glasses, depending on the occasion. The Louisiana-style remoulade really makes it.

TO MAKE THE REMOULADE: Whisk together all the ingredients in a bowl. Makes 1½ cups. Cover and refrigerate for at least 1 hour or up to several days.

TO MAKE THE SLAW: Combine ½ cup of the remoulade, both cabbages, and the pepitas in a large bowl and toss well. Add the shrimp, lobster, and at least ½ cup remoulade and toss again. Refrigerate the slaw and remaining remoulade for at least 1 hour. Arrange the slaw on plates, drizzle with more remoulade if you wish, and serve.

Roasted Salmon with Tomato-Caper Relish

SERVES 6 TO 8

TOMATO-CAPER RELISH

8 to 10 ounces grape tomatoes, halved

1 medium shallot, thinly sliced

2 tablespoons drained capers

2 tablespoons red wine vinegar

¼ teaspoon kosher salt

One 2½- to 3-pound skin-on salmon fillet

4 tablespoons olive oil

Kosher salt

1 to 2 tablespoons chopped fresh rosemary leaves

SEAFOOD SALAD WITH CREAMY DRESSING

||||||||||||||||||||||||||||||

Skip the cabbage and pepitas; instead, mix the lobster and shrimp with a couple of diced celery stalks, about 1 cup halved seedless red grapes, and at least ½ cup of this creamy dressing: Mix together 1 scant cup mayonnaise, 1 heaping tablespoon minced fresh chives, ½ teaspoon lemon juice, and a good pinch each of salt and pepper. If you wish, serve each portion over a leaf of butter lettuce, and drizzle with any additional dressing.

While we're all about beef at Perini Ranch Steakhouse, we do offer salmon with a colorful, Italian-inspired topping at parties we cater. The dish can be served warm or prepared ahead and served at room temperature or chilled.

TO START THE RELISH: Gently combine the tomatoes, shallot, capers, vinegar, and salt in a bowl. Let stand at room temperature for 30 minutes.

Heat the oven to 375°F. Arrange the salmon, skin side down, on a parchment paper–lined baking sheet. Brush the salmon with 2 tablespoons of the oil and sprinkle with the salt and rosemary.

Bake the salmon for 12 to 15 minutes, until lightly crisp on top and still somewhat translucent in the center when pierced with a knife.

While the salmon is baking, finish the relish: Heat the remaining 2 tablespoons olive oil in a skillet over medium heat. Stir in the tomato-caper mixture and sauté until the tomatoes are heated throughout and just limp, about 2 minutes. Set aside while the salmon finishes cooking.

The salmon can be served hot or at room temperature. Using a spatula, transfer the salmon to a platter and spoon the relish over the top.

SIDE DISHES

Zucchini Perini

½ pound ground beef

½ pound ground Italian pork sausage, preferably hot

1 large onion, finely diced

One 28-ounce can whole tomatoes, drained and cut into pieces

One 6-ounce can tomato paste

¼ cup tomato sauce

2 teaspoons crumbled dried oregano

⅛ teaspoon garlic powder

2 pounds zucchini, sliced into ¼-inch-thick rounds

Kosher salt and freshly ground black pepper

¼ cup grated Parmigiano-Reggiano

½ cup Bread Crumbs (page 150) or toasted panko bread crumbs

2½ tablespoons dried parsley

Has a nice ring to it, doesn't it? We think the smile the name brings gets some folks who might otherwise skip over vegetables to give it a try.

Since zucchini grows like—well, zucchini—in Texas in the warm months, it's really handy to have a good recipe to use them up. Turn your head for a minute, and those petite hand-sized zukes turn into baseball bats.

Heat the oven to 350°F.

In a large, oven-safe skillet, sauté the ground beef, sausage, and onion over medium-high heat until the meat is evenly browned, and the onion is limp, 5 to 8 minutes. Stir in the tomatoes, tomato paste, and tomato sauce and mix well. Stir in the oregano and garlic powder. Reduce the heat to medium and simmer for 5 minutes. Stir in the zucchini and season with salt and pepper. Continue cooking just until the zucchini wilts, about 5 minutes. Sprinkle the Parmigiano on top.

Transfer the skillet to the oven and bake for 10 to 12 minutes, until the zucchini is fork-tender and the cheese has melted and browned in spots. Remove from the oven. Combine the bread crumbs and parsley and scatter the mixture evenly over the zucchini. Let sit for 5 minutes before serving.

Bourbon-Glazed Carrots

SERVES 6

1 pound baby carrots

½ teaspoon kosher salt,
plus more to taste

¼ cup packed brown sugar

¼ teaspoon ground cinnamon

Pinch or 2 cayenne

¼ cup coarsely chopped pecans

4 tablespoons salted butter,
cut up into small pieces

2 tablespoons bourbon

You want to get a cowboy—or just about anyone else—to eat a vegetable? Cover it in bourbon and brown sugar. Luckily that's a winning combination when it comes to carrots. We use our special Perini Ranch Steakhouse Private Select Maker's Mark, but any bourbon you drink is fine.

Bring a medium saucepan of water to a boil. Add the carrots and salt, reduce the heat to a simmer, and cook for 8 to 10 minutes, until the carrots can just be pierced with a fork. Drain in a colander and return the carrots to the pan.

While the carrots are cooking, stir together the brown sugar, cinnamon, and cayenne in a bowl. Toast the pecans in a dry skillet over medium-low heat, stirring often so they don't burn, until they are aromatic. Set aside.

Stir the butter into the warm carrots and return to low heat. When melted, add the bourbon, then stir in the brown sugar mixture. Continue cooking, stirring frequently, until the carrots are glazed and tender. Add salt to taste. Top the glazed carrots with the pecans and serve.

Yellow Squash Casserole

4 tablespoons (½ stick) salted butter, at room temperature

1 large sweet onion, halved from top to bottom, then sliced ⅛ inch thick, preferably on a mandoline

2 large eggs, beaten

¼ cup whole milk

1 teaspoon kosher salt

½ teaspoon freshly ground black pepper

2½ pounds yellow summer squash, sliced ¼ inch thick, preferably on a mandoline

2½ cups (10 ounces) shredded medium or sharp Cheddar

¼ cup panko bread crumbs, toasted in a dry skillet

½ cup chopped fresh basil leaves

Nothing is more exciting to a gardener than the first picking of tiny, tender yellow squash. Nothing is less exciting than the 98th picking of that same squash. Here's the traditional Texas way of smothering summer squash (or other vegetables) in casseroles with cheese, but the fresh basil makes it especially wonderful. It's as delicious as it is popular.

Heat the oven to 375°F. Grease a 9x13-inch baking dish with 1 tablespoon of the butter.

Melt the remaining 3 tablespoons of butter in a large skillet over medium heat. Stir in the onion and sauté until tender and translucent. Cool briefly.

Whisk together the eggs, milk, salt, and pepper in a large bowl. Stir in the cooked onion, squash, 2 cups of the Cheddar, half of the bread crumbs, and half of the basil. Spoon the mixture into the baking dish. Scatter the remaining ½ cup Cheddar, ¼ cup bread crumbs, and ¼ cup basil over the squash mixture. Cover the casserole with aluminum foil.

Bake for 30 minutes. Remove the foil and continue baking for an additional 15 minutes, until the squash is tender and the casserole is bubbly. Let sit for 5 to 10 minutes before serving.

Mesquite Grilled Eggplant Parmesan

SERVES 8

2 tablespoons olive oil, plus more for the eggplant and the baking dish

½ cup diced onion

2 garlic cloves, minced

One 28-ounce can whole peeled tomatoes, such as Cento brand

1½ teaspoons dried oregano

½ teaspoon red pepper flakes

1 large eggplant, cut into ¼-inch-thick slices

1 teaspoon kosher salt

1 teaspoon freshly ground black pepper

8 ounces mozzarella, cubed

½ cup thinly sliced fresh basil leaves

½ cup panko bread crumbs

½ cup grated Parmigiano-Reggiano

Lots of eggplant Parmesan recipes call for breading and frying the eggplant before assembling the casserole. But we found that grilling the eggplant slices makes them tender rather than heavy, adds a note of rusticity from the mesquite coals' light smoke, and makes this recipe unique to Perini Ranch. While traveling in Italy, we took a cooking class that featured eggplant Parmesan. We're more convinced than ever that mesquite-grilling the eggplant is the way to go. This dish is a great blend of Tom's Italian heritage and real Texas cooking.

Heat the oven to 400°F.

Warm the oil in a medium saucepan over medium heat. Stir in the onion and garlic. Cook, stirring frequently, until the onions are tender. Add the tomatoes, cutting them up with a spoon or crushing them with your fingers as they go into the pan. Stir in the oregano and red pepper flakes. Simmer the sauce for 10 minutes to thicken.

Fire up the grill, bringing the temperature to medium (4 to 5 seconds with the hand test—see page 81). For the best flavor if cooking over gas or charcoal, add a half-dozen mesquite chunks to the fire a few minutes before placing the eggplant on the grill.

Lightly brush the eggplant slices with olive oil and season with salt and pepper. Grill the eggplant slices about 4 minutes per side, until limp. They will cook further when baked.

Brush a 9x13-inch baking dish with olive oil. Spread 1 cup tomato sauce in the bottom of the dish. Top with about one-third of the eggplant, followed by half of the mozzarella and half of the basil. Repeat with the tomato sauce, eggplant, mozzarella, and basil. Top the second layer with the remaining eggplant and tomato sauce. Evenly sprinkle the panko and Parmigiano on top.

Bake for 30 minutes, until heated through and bubbly on top. Increase the oven temperature to 500°F and bake for an additional 5 minutes to brown the top. Let sit for 5 to 10 minutes before serving.

Grilled Asparagus

SERVES 6

1½ pounds asparagus spears, preferably medium-thick, trimmed of tough ends

Extra virgin olive oil

Kosher salt and freshly ground black pepper

One of the best practical jokes ever played on Tom was by Mario Espino, our ranch manager of more than twenty years. Tom had been nursing along a bed of asparagus in our Steakhouse garden. Some of you will know that asparagus takes about three years to root and shoot up, in a quantity that amounts to a meal. Tom was really excited by year three, checking the bed once or twice a day, ready to harvest his first crop. One morning, dozens of asparagus spears had shot up overnight. Why, they were 6, 8, 10 inches tall! Lisa was back at the house and got a call: "Get down here now. The asparagus has done it!" There was much marveling at the crop, though it started to sink in that it looked just a tad too perfect. When Tom went closer to investigate, he discovered that Mario had stuck a whole passel of grocery store asparagus into the ground overnight.

Fire up the grill, bringing the temperature to medium (4 to 5 seconds with the hand test—see page 81). For the best flavor if cooking over gas or charcoal, add a half-dozen mesquite chunks to the fire a few minutes before placing the asparagus on the grill.

Toss the asparagus in a shallow dish with enough oil to coat lightly. Sprinkle with salt and pepper.

Transfer the asparagus to the grill, perpendicular to the cooking grate and placing the stems over the hottest part of the fire and the tips toward an outer edge. Grill uncovered for 5 to 8 minutes, depending on the thickness, rolling them frequently to cook on all sides. Serve warm or at room temperature, perhaps with another drizzle of oil and an extra sprinkling of salt and pepper.

Fried Okra

1½ pounds small okra, sliced into ½-inch-thick rings

2 teaspoons kosher salt

Vegetable oil for pan-frying

1 cup all-purpose flour

1 cup dry bread crumbs

1 teaspoon granulated garlic

1 teaspoon celery salt

1 teaspoon freshly ground black pepper

Every true Southerner loves okra, and frying is the best method of cooking this vegetable. Fried okra should be delectably crunchy, almost like popcorn.

In a bowl, cover the okra with ice water and stir in 1 teaspoon salt to keep the okra crisp. Let the okra soak at room temperature for 15 to 30 minutes.

Clip a deep-fry thermometer to the inside of a deep 12- or 14-inch cast-iron skillet or Dutch oven. Pour in oil to a depth 1½ to 2 inches and bring to 325°F over medium-high heat. Line a baking sheet with paper towels. Put a wire baking rack on top of the paper towels.

Combine the flour, bread crumbs, granulated garlic, celery salt, remaining 1 teaspoon salt, and the pepper on a shallow plate.

Drain the okra in a colander, but do not dry completely. Coat the damp okra with the breading, then transfer to a strainer and shake off any excess. Using a large slotted spoon, lower about one-half of the okra into the hot oil. Don't overcrowd the skillet. Fry the okra just until golden, 1 to 2 minutes. Stir occasionally to fry evenly. Drain the okra on the wire rack. Continue to fry the remaining okra. Serve hot.

Fire-Roasted Vegetables

SERVES 6 OR MORE

½ cup extra virgin olive oil

½ teaspoon kosher salt

¼ teaspoon freshly ground black pepper

VEGETABLES

1 large red onion, cut into ⅓-inch-thick rounds

1 large sweet onion, cut into ⅓-inch-thick rounds

8 ounces small mushroom caps

1 medium eggplant, cut into ½-inch-thick rounds

3 or 4 red or yellow bell peppers, halved and seeded

3 or 4 New Mexican green or poblano chiles, halved and seeded

Green onions, any limp green tops cut off

1 or 2 zucchini or yellow squash, cut lengthwise into ½-inch-thick pieces

2 sweet potatoes, peeled and cut into ⅓-inch-thick rounds

Olive oil spray or vegetable oil spray

Francis Mallmann, the visionary Argentinian chef, was our guest at the three-day 2014 Buffalo Gap Wine & Food Summit. Francis has a collection of techniques for cooking with wood and coals that he details in his book *Seven Fires*. For his visit, we fabricated all seven fires, which included a variety of grills, cooking surfaces, and iron baskets for burning wood down to coals. Our ranch crew dug trenches and pits. It was a hazy, smoke-tinged, other-worldly scene for days. After cooking whole animals and other big hunks of protein, we cooked whole onions, bell peppers, sweet potatoes, butternut squash, and other vegetables in embers, capturing every bit of the dying fire's heat.

But unless you're already planning to cook a few lambs, sides of beef, or massively large fish and expect to have loads of hot ash, we figured a simple grilling of smaller vegetable slices will serve you better. We just love the earthy flavors and colors grill-roasted vegetables bring to the plate. Pick out four or five of the vegetables listed and make a big platter.

You can use metal or bamboo skewers for the onions. If using bamboo, soak them in water for 20 minutes so they don't burn on the grill.

Whisk the oil, salt, and pepper together in a bowl.

Fire up the grill, bringing the temperature to medium (4 to 5 seconds with the hand test—see page 81). For the best flavor if cooking over gas or charcoal, add a half-dozen mesquite chunks to the fire a few minutes before grilling.

Thread skewers through the red and sweet onion slices. Spray all of the vegetables on all sides with oil.

Grill the vegetables, uncovered, over medium heat, rotating them a half turn each time for grill marks and scattering on the salt as they cook on each side, until tender. This will take 8 to 10 minutes for the mushroom caps; 10 to 12 minutes for the eggplant, peppers, chiles, and green onions; 12 to 15 minutes for the zucchini or yellow squash; and 18 to 20 minutes for the sweet potatoes and onion slices, turning all of them twice on each side. As the vegetables finish, transfer them to a platter. Slide the onions off the skewers and pull any loose skins from the bell peppers and chiles and thinly slice. Drizzle with the seasoned oil, as desired, and serve.

Roasted Corn on the Cob with Chile-Lime Butter

SERVES 6 OR MORE

CHILE-LIME BUTTER

1 cup (2 sticks) salted butter

Juice of 1 lime

Pinch of cayenne

6 to 8 fresh ears of corn

Kosher salt and freshly ground black pepper

Is there anything that says summer as emphatically and deliciously as corn on the cob? Cooking ears in their husks over the grill adds an extra touch of showmanship and flavor.

Fire up the grill, bringing the temperature to medium (4 to 5 seconds with the hand test—see page 81). For the best flavor if cooking over gas or charcoal, add a half-dozen mesquite chunks to the fire a few minutes before grilling the corn.

TO MAKE THE CHILE-LIME BUTTER: Melt the butter with the lime juice and cayenne in a wide, shallow pan (for rolling the ears of corn). Once melted, keep the butter warm.

Remove all but the last 3 or 4 husks from each ear of corn but keep them attached at the end. The corn silks will dry while the corn is on the grill and will easily pull away from the cobs. (Save several of the longer, stronger husks and shred into ½-inch strips to tie back the other husks on the cooked ears of corn.) Put the corn on the grill and cook, turning on all sides with tongs for a total of 8 to 10 minutes. When done, the corn kernels should be tender but still a bit firm when pierced with a fork, and kissed with flecks of brown from the fire. Wearing mitts, pull back the husks and discard the silks. Tie back the husks that remain on each cob with the strips of reserved corn husk.

Using tongs, roll each hot ear of corn in the warm butter. Offer salt and pepper at the table. Serve hot with plenty of napkins.

ROASTING AND PEELING GREEN CHILES

||||||||||||||||||||||||||||||||||||||||||||||||||||

Chiles and peppers are best when they are roasted and their skins are removed. This can easily be done in an oven, on top of a gas stove, or on an outdoor grill.

To roast in the oven, heat the oven to 450°F. Arrange the chiles in a single layer on a baking sheet and roast until blistered and blackened on all sides, turning them as necessary until they collapse.

If you are roasting only a couple of chiles or peppers, use tongs and hold them over the flame of a gas burner for a few minutes, until they blacken on all sides.

Chiles and peppers can also be roasted on the grate of a charcoal, gas, or wood-burning grill. Sear on all sides for 10 minutes.

Once the chiles or peppers are roasted, immediately place them in a plastic bag and seal, or place in a bowl and cover with foil. Let them sit for 5 to 10 minutes, or until cool enough to handle. Put on disposable gloves if dealing with chiles. This is to avoid getting capsaicin, the substance that gives chiles their heat, on your hands. It doesn't wash off easily and can irritate the skin. Using your gloved fingers, strip off the skins. If a bit of blackened skin remains, that's fine. Avoid running water over the chiles, because their flavor will become diluted. Remove the stems and seeds and slice or chop the chiles as needed.

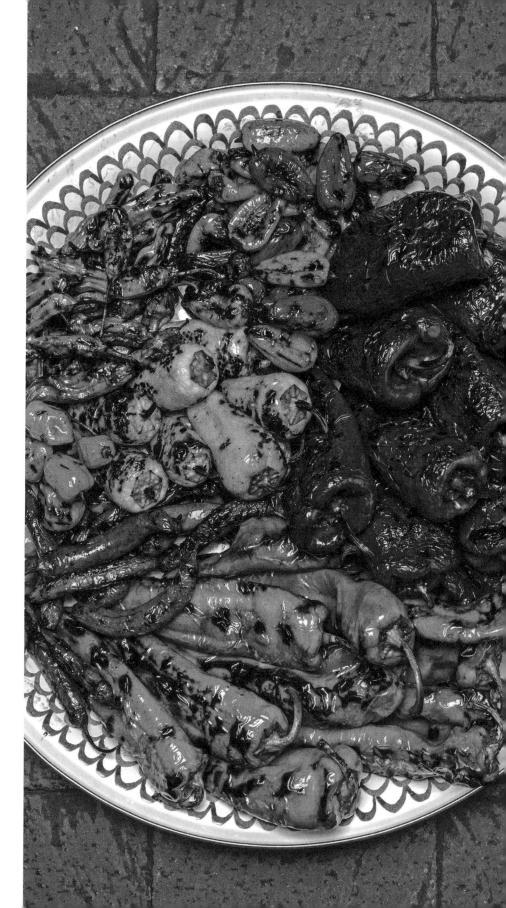

Roasted Corn and Poblano Pudding

Vegetable oil spray

6 thick slices bacon

¾ cup (1½ sticks) unsalted butter

¾ cup chopped onion

½ teaspoon kosher salt

½ teaspoon freshly ground black pepper

2 poblano peppers, roasted, peeled, seeded, and diced (see sidebar, opposite)

5 cups grill-roasted corn kernels (from 5 ears; see page 128)

¾ cup heavy whipping cream

One 8-ounce package cream cheese, cut into cubes, at room temperature

¾ cup grated Parmigiano-Reggiano

3 large eggs

⅓ cup whole milk

Corn and chiles go together like tequila and limes. A poblano is a fresh green chile similar in heat to the New Mexican green chile. The deeper green poblanos take their name from the Mexican city of Puebla and are distinguished by their broad "shoulders." The flavor is a bit earthier than the slimmer New Mexican pods. This recipe is decadent, rich, and almost a meal by itself. While it's one of our newer menu additions, this side already has a huge following. Many have requested this recipe—here it is!

Heat the oven to 350°F. Spray a 9x13-inch baking dish with vegetable oil spray.

Put the bacon slices in a large, cold skillet. Turn the heat to medium-low and cook the bacon for 3 minutes on one side. Turn the bacon and cook on the other side to desired doneness. Remove the bacon with a slotted spoon and drain on paper towels. When cool enough to handle, crumble the bacon with your fingers and set aside. Discard all but 2 tablespoons of the bacon fat.

Add the butter, onion, salt, and pepper to the bacon drippings in the skillet and cook over medium heat until the onions are soft. Add the poblanos, corn, cream, cream cheese, and Parmigiano, stirring well to combine.

Whisk together the eggs and milk in a bowl. Add about ½ cup of the hot corn mixture to the eggs, so the eggs won't scramble. Add the egg mixture to the corn mixture and stir well. Pour the corn mixture into the prepared dish and stir in the bacon. Cover with aluminum foil and bake for 45 minutes. Uncover and bake for an additional 10 minutes, until the top browns. Let sit for 10 minutes before serving.

A Mess of Greens with Potlikker

SERVES 8

1 pound fresh collard greens

1 pound fresh mustard greens

1 pound fresh turnip greens

4 cups low-sodium chicken stock

¾ teaspoon kosher salt

¾ teaspoon freshly ground black pepper

Tabasco or other hot pepper sauce

Cut off the greens' stem ends from the leaves. Chop the leaves of the greens into 3-inch pieces.

Combine the stock, 4 cups of water, salt, and pepper in a large pot and bring to a boil over high heat. Add the greens to the pot, pushing them down into the liquid with a large spoon. Cover and reduce the heat to medium. Cook the greens for at least 20 minutes, stirring occasionally. (If the liquid evaporates, add some more water or stock. The greens should always be submerged.) Pierce the greens with a fork to check for tenderness. For softer greens, cook for an additional 10 minutes. Serve the greens spooned out into bowls with some of the potlikker. Pass the hot pepper sauce at the table.

If you didn't grow up somewhere between Texas and South Carolina, you may not know that the term "mess" refers—in Southern food terms—to a large batch of something, most often greens. These three voluminous greens (collard, mustard, and turnip) all wilt down substantially during cooking. The liquid in which greens or other vegetables are simmered is called "potlikker," a magical elixir full of vitamins from the greens cooked in it. You just might catch Tom in the kitchen, dunking a coffee mug into the greens for a little of the potlikker.

Ranch Manager Mario Espino with fresh-picked greens.

Southern Sweet Potatoes with Brown Sugar Pecans

SERVES 6 TO 8

SWEET POTATOES

Vegetable oil spray

3 pounds sweet potatoes, preferably Garnet or another deeply colored variety

1 cup granulated sugar

6 tablespoons (¾ stick) salted butter

½ cup whole milk

3 large eggs, lightly beaten

1½ teaspoons pure vanilla extract

BROWN SUGAR PECAN TOPPING

1 cup chopped pecans

1 cup packed brown sugar

Scant ½ cup all-purpose flour

¼ cup (½ stick) salted butter, melted

Regular Steakhouse guests start asking, usually about halfway through football season, when this fall favorite will be on the menu. We usually wait until just before Thanksgiving to roll it out. Credit goes to Lisa's mom for this holiday treat, sweet enough to serve for dessert. In addition to catering, we do a brisk business in big take-out trays of some of our staples, and these sweet potatoes are one of our most popular offerings.

TO MAKE THE SWEET POTATOES: Heat the oven to 350°F. Spray a 9x13-inch shallow baking dish with vegetable oil spray.

Use a fork to poke holes in each sweet potato. Put the sweet potatoes on a baking sheet and bake for 50 to 60 minutes, until very tender when pierced with a fork. Remove the sweet potatoes and leave the oven on.

When cool enough to handle, cut each potato open lengthwise and scoop out the flesh—it should slide right out—into a bowl. Discard the peels. Mash the flesh well with a potato masher and add the granulated sugar, butter, milk, eggs, and vanilla. With a hand mixer on medium speed, beat to combine until the mixture is thin, light, and fluffy. Spoon the mixture into the prepared baking dish.

TO MAKE THE TOPPING: Stir the pecans, brown sugar, and flour together in a bowl. Stir in the melted butter until well combined. Spread the topping over the sweet potatoes.

Bake for 35 to 45 minutes, until the pecan topping is crunchy and the sweet potato mixture is hot and bubbly throughout. Serve hot.

Old-Fashioned Green Beans

SERVES 6 TO 8

Two 28-ounce cans Allens Seasoned Cut Italian Green Beans or other canned cut Italian green beans

⅔ cup minced white onion

1½ to 2 tablespoons bacon drippings or vegetable oil

½ teaspoon freshly ground black pepper

Kosher salt

Old-fashioned green beans generally are long-cooked to delectable tenderness with seasonings such as bacon drippings and a good hit of black pepper. We start with already tender canned Italian-style green beans, then add more zip to them.

Combine the beans and their liquid, onion, bacon drippings, and pepper in a large saucepan. Bring to a boil, then reduce to a simmer and cook about 10 minutes, until the onion is tender. Season with salt to taste.

Turn off the heat and let the beans sit for 15 minutes for the flavors to meld. Reheat if you wish, and serve the beans in small bowls with some of the juices.

BACON DRIPPINGS

|||||||||||||||||||||||||||||||||||

Up until a generation ago, cooks kept an old coffee can or small crock of bacon drippings, poured off from the cast-iron skillet from frying each morning's bacon. No one ever refrigerated the drippings back in the day. They were just kept under the sink or on top of the stove to be used to grease the skillet for cornbread, vegetables, and chicken-fried steak. Drippings were considered liquid gold, a kitchen gift that just kept on giving.

If you want to save the flavorful fat, keep it in the fridge to make sure it doesn't spoil. Some folks go to the effort of straining the drippings when pouring them into the storage container, but we don't bother.

Twice-Baked Potato Casserole

SERVES 8

2 pounds russet potatoes

2 or 3 thick slices bacon

Vegetable oil spray

1 cup (4 ounces) shredded Cheddar

2 ounces cream cheese, softened

8 ounces sour cream

¼ cup whole milk

¼ cup (½ stick) salted butter, melted

1 garlic clove, minced

¾ teaspoon kosher salt

½ teaspoon freshly ground black pepper

½ cup thinly sliced green onion tops, light and dark green portions

We don't serve baked potatoes or French fries. When Tom opened the steakhouse, he was committed to offering unique sides, like Green Chile Hominy (page 140) and Zucchini Perini (page 119). We like to think our sides are as popular and crowd pleasing as our entrees. This potato casserole has all the baked potato toppings, so no decisions need to be made.

Heat the oven to 375°F. Butter a 9x13-inch baking dish at least 2 inches deep.

Use a fork to prick a few holes in each potato. Put the potatoes directly on the center oven rack. Bake for 45 to 60 minutes (depending on their size), until they can easily be pierced with a fork.

While the potatoes are baking, cook the bacon: Put the bacon slices in a cold skillet. Turn the heat to medium-low and cook the bacon for 3 minutes on one side. Turn the bacon and cook on the other side to desired doneness. Remove the bacon with a slotted spoon and drain on paper towels. When cool enough to handle, use your hands to break the bacon into small pieces.

Remove the potatoes, leaving the oven on. When the potatoes are cool enough to handle, cut them in half and scoop out the flesh into a bowl. Using a potato masher, mash the potatoes well. Stir in the Cheddar, cream cheese, sour cream, milk, and butter. Mix in the bacon, garlic, salt, pepper, and ¼ cup of the green onions.

Evenly spoon the mixture into the baking dish. Bake for 30 to 35 minutes, until heated through and bubbly. Let rest for 5 to 10 minutes. Scatter the remaining ¼ cup green onions on top before serving.

Cowboy Potatoes

SERVES 8 OR MORE

4 pounds red waxy potatoes such as Red Bliss, cut into thick wedges

½ cup (1 stick) salted butter, melted

1 medium white onion, thinly sliced

1 or 2 garlic cloves, minced

1 teaspoon kosher salt

1 teaspoon freshly ground black pepper

½ teaspoon crumbled dried oregano

Here's the side dish most popular with our cowboys and ranchers—kind of elemental in its preparation and in its appeal. For a buffet, serve them up in a hefty cast-iron skillet. Nothing beats these when it comes to a steak-and-potato meal.

Heat the oven to 350°F.

In a large shallow bowl, toss together the potato wedges, butter, onion, garlic, salt, pepper, and oregano. Spoon into a shallow baking dish and cover with aluminum foil.

Bake for 1 hour, stirring occasionally. Remove the foil and continue baking for another 30 minutes. The potatoes should be lightly crusted in spots and tender when pierced with a fork. Let rest for 5 to 10 minutes before serving.

Mashed Potatoes

3 pounds russet or other large baking potatoes

1½ tablespoons kosher salt, or more to taste

¾ cup (1½ sticks) salted butter

¾ cup heavy whipping cream

¾ teaspoon freshly ground black pepper

If there isn't a Texas state law requiring that mashed potatoes be served with chicken-fried steak and fried chicken (often referred to around these parts as chicken-fried chicken) and topped with some cream gravy, there ought to be. Ours are classic with a bit of a rustic look, because we leave on some of the peel and mash them by hand so there are some small potato chunks. Of course, mashed potatoes can accompany just about anything—grilled steak, braised short ribs, or fried chicken.

Wash the potatoes and partially peel them, leaving about half of the peels in place, then cut into 2-inch chunks. Combine them in a large pot with enough water to cover by at least an inch and the salt. Bring to a boil over high heat, then reduce the heat to medium and cook until quite tender, 15 to 20 minutes. When done, the exteriors of the potato chunks should be crumbly, almost dissolving in spots.

While the potatoes cook, heat the butter and cream together in a saucepan, just until bubbles form around the edge.

Drain the potatoes, then return to the warm pot. Drizzle in the warm butter-cream mixture, mashing the potatoes with a potato masher as you go. Leave a few small chunks of potato. Season with pepper and, if you wish, more salt. Serve piping hot.

BLUE CHEESE MASHED POTATOES
Prepare the potatoes as above, using only 1½ teaspoons salt in the cooking water. When you add the cream-butter mixture, stir in ½ to ¾ cup room-temperature blue cheese crumbles, preferably a mild Danish blue cheese. Taste for seasoning and serve.

Black-Eyed Peas with Bacon and Jalapeños

SERVES 6 TO 8

2 slices thick bacon

Three 15.5-ounce cans black-eyed peas, drained, liquid reserved from 1 can

1 or 2 pickled jalapeños, chopped

Kosher salt, to taste

Put the bacon slices in a cold skillet. Turn the heat to medium-low and cook the bacon for 3 minutes on one side. Turn the bacon and cook on the other side to desired doneness. Remove the bacon with a slotted spoon and drain on paper towels. Save the bacon drippings in the skillet. When cool enough to handle, crumble the bacon with your fingers and set aside.

Add the crumbled bacon, peas and reserved liquid, and jalapeños to the bacon drippings in the skillet. Taste and add salt, if you wish. Cook over medium heat for 5 minutes for the flavors to blend. Serve hot.

A favorite Southern tradition, eating black-eyed peas on the first day of the new year, has long been associated with good luck for the coming year. Once, when we were visiting Fess Parker and his family at their winery in California's Santa Ynez wine region over the New Year's holiday, we were flabbergasted to learn that our friends had no knowledge of this tradition. There were no black-eyed peas to be found within miles of their home. Ever since, when traveling over New Year's, we make sure we pack a few cans of black-eyed peas. While black-eyed peas go particularly well with fried catfish (page 110), you can serve them with just about anything.

FESS PARKER

||||||||||||||||||||||||

Texas native Fess Parker became one of the mid-century's most beloved television stars, known internationally for playing American icons Davy Crockett and Daniel Boone. He walked away from that lucrative career in the early 1970s to grow grapes and make fine wines under his name. As a result, he became just as big a star in the wine world as he had been in Hollywood. His family has continued the winemaking tradition along what is now known as the Foxen Canyon Wine Trail near Los Olivos, California. Fess passed away in 2010. We miss his charm, straight-talking style, and wisdom. Our friendship now spans three generations. You can order the families' wines online at fessparker.com.

Green Chile Hominy

SERVES 10 TO 12

Vegetable oil spray

10 slices bacon

1 cup chopped onion

Four 15-ounce cans white hominy, drained, with ½ cup liquid reserved

1 or 2 pickled jalapeños, minced, with 1 tablespoon liquid from the jar

1 cup chopped, roasted, peeled, and seeded New Mexican green or poblano chiles (see sidebar, page 130)

8 ounces (2 cups) shredded Cheddar

If you only make one recipe from this book besides a steak, it should be this hominy. Not only is it a Steakhouse signature, on the menu from almost day one, but it works equally well for breakfast and dinner. Tom created the dish when working with the late Louise Matthews of Albany, Texas. Mrs. Matthews held an epic party in conjunction with the Fort Griffin Fandangle, the oldest outdoor musical production in Texas, which showcases ranching life in West Central Texas with music and merriment. You can assemble the hominy dish a day ahead.

Heat the oven to 350°F. Spray a 9x13-inch baking dish at least 2 inches deep with vegetable oil spray.

Put the bacon slices in a cold skillet. Turn the heat to medium-low and cook the bacon for 3 minutes on one side. Turn the bacon and cook on the other side to desired doneness. Remove the bacon with a slotted spoon and drain on paper towels.

When cool enough to handle, crumble the bacon with your fingers and set aside.

Carefully pour off all but 2 to 3 table-spoons of the bacon drippings. Return the skillet to the stovetop and stir in the onion. Cook over medium heat until the onion is tender, 5 minutes. Pour in the hominy liquid and jalapeño liquid and cook until reduced by about one-half, about 5 minutes. Add the hominy and jalapeños and heat through. Stir in half of the crumbled bacon and half of the cheese.

Spoon into the prepared baking dish. Scatter the remaining bacon and cheese over the hominy. Bake for 25 minutes, until the cheese on top melts and the hominy mixture is bubbly. Let sit for 5 minutes before serving.

Jalapeño Cheese Grits

SERVES 6 OR MORE

1 large egg, well-beaten

2 tablespoons heavy whipping cream (preferably), half-and-half, or whole milk

¾ cup (6 ounces) shredded mild Cheddar

⅓ cup minced and seeded jalapeños

4 cups low-sodium chicken stock

¼ cup (½ stick) salted butter

1 cup quick-cooking grits, such as Quaker

Kosher salt (optional)

Nothing illustrates South by Southwest fare better than cheesy grits laced with jalapeño. With Lisa's Southern roots, it's the ultimate comfort food at our house served for breakfast, lunch, or dinner.

While store-bought chicken stock is a great timesaver, try making your own (see below) for the best flavor.

Heat the oven to 350°F. Butter a shallow 7x11-inch baking dish.

Combine the egg, cream, Cheddar, and jalapeños in a bowl and mix.

Combine the stock and butter in a large saucepan and bring to a boil over high heat. Over 2 to 3 minutes, sprinkle in the grits, about ¼ cup at a time, whisking continually to eliminate any lumps. Reduce the heat to a simmer. Switch from a whisk to a rubber spatula and continue to cook, stirring frequently, for 5 minutes, until the grits are thickened and coat the back of the spatula. Spoon out a teaspoon of the grits, let cool briefly, and taste for salt. Add more as necessary. Remove the saucepan from the heat and stir in the egg-jalapeño-cheese mixture. Pour the grits into the prepared baking dish.

Cover the dish with aluminum foil and bake for 30 minutes. Uncover and bake for an additional 10 minutes, until the grits are lightly puffed and golden. Let rest for 5 to 10 minutes before serving.

MAKING STOCK

For homemade chicken stock, use this as a guide. Add less onion or more carrot, for example, depending upon what you have on hand, and your wishes.

Warm 2 tablespoons olive oil in a large stockpot over medium-high heat. Working in two batches, add 3 pounds chicken parts (backs, wings, wing tips, thighs, and/or legs), skin side down. Brown well, then turn and brown the other side. Remove from the pot and brown the remaining chicken. Return the first batch to the pot and add 1 large yellow onion, quartered; 1 large carrot and 1 celery rib (including the leaves), both cut in 2-inch pieces; 1 bunch parsley; and a couple of bay leaves. Cover with about 5 quarts cold water. Bring to a boil over high heat, then reduce to a simmer. Cook uncovered for 3 to 4 hours, skimming off any scum and fat that rise to the top, until richly flavored. Place a colander over another large pot and carefully pour in the hot stock and solids. Press down on the solids to get out all of the goodness, then discard the solids. Bring the stock to a boil over high heat, then reduce the heat. Simmer until the stock is reduced to about 6 cups. Let cool, then refrigerate for up to a week, or freeze for up to several months.

Ranch Pintos

SERVES 6 TO 8

1 pound dried pinto beans, sorted through for any stones or dirt, then rinsed

¼ pound salt pork or bacon, chopped

3 or 4 garlic cloves, minced

1 tablespoon chili powder

Kosher salt

Nothing's more essential to ranch and chuck wagon cooking than a hearty pot of pinto beans. This is because preserved salt pork as well as dried beans could be carried along the trail to easily make a hearty, stick-to-the-ribs filler that could be flavored up in different ways. You may not be out on a cattle drive, but if you have a pot of beans, you too have dinner. And perhaps in the time-honored way: a bowl of pintos with a wedge of cornbread. Or strain and spoon the beans into a flour tortilla and build a burrito. Pinto beans are also a good side with any pork dish or Texas barbecue.

Put the beans in a large stockpot or Dutch oven and cover with cold water by at least 2 inches. Add the salt pork and garlic and bring to a boil over high heat. Reduce the heat to a simmer and cook the beans, uncovered, until they are creamy and tender, up to 2 hours. Check the beans several times during the cooking, stirring them up from the bottom. Add hot water as needed to keep the water level at least an inch above the beans.

Stir the chili powder and salt to taste into the beans and cook over low heat for another 15 minutes. There should be some liquid remaining in the pot.

Serve warm with two or more spoonfuls of the potlikker. The beans can be refrigerated and kept for several days; they are even better when reheated.

Mac 'n' Cheese with Roasted Poblanos

SERVES 8

BREAD CRUMBS

1 tablespoon olive oil

1 cup panko bread crumbs

CHEESE SAUCE

½ cup (1 stick) salted butter

2 tablespoons all-purpose flour

1 garlic clove, minced

1 cup whole milk

½ cup heavy whipping cream

¾ teaspoon kosher salt

2 cups (8 ounces) shredded sharp Cheddar

4 ounces fresh goat cheese, crumbled

¼ cup grated Parmigiano-Reggiano

¼ cup buttermilk, sour cream, or plain full-fat yogurt

MACARONI

2 teaspoons kosher salt

¾ pound (12 ounces) elbow macaroni

2 poblano chiles, roasted, peeled, seeded, and chopped (see page 130)

We were asked to cater a Texas wedding where the bride had her heart set on serving macaroni and cheese. We had never thought of serving mac 'n' cheese alongside our Mesquite Smoked Peppered Beef Tenderloin, but she was determined. If you're going to serve mac 'n' cheese, it has to be a really good one, and here it is! The dish was such a hit with the bride, groom, and their families and guests that we ended up serving it at the weddings of the bride's three sisters.

Heat the oven to 375°F. Butter a 9x13-inch baking dish.

TO TOAST THE BREAD CRUMBS: Warm the oil in a small skillet over medium heat. Stir in the panko and toast until golden, stirring frequently. Turn off the heat and set aside.

TO MAKE THE SAUCE: Melt the butter in a large saucepan over medium-low heat. Whisk the flour into the butter until incorporated, then cook for 2 to 3 minutes, stirring frequently. Stir in the garlic, raise the heat to medium-high, and gradually whisk in the milk and cream. Add the salt. Bring the mixture to a boil and continue to stir until thickened, about 4 minutes. Reduce the heat to medium-low and stir in the Cheddar, goat cheese, and Parmigiano. Remove from the heat as soon as the cheeses have melted. Stir in the buttermilk. Cover to keep the sauce warm.

TO MAKE THE MACARONI: Bring a large pot of water to a boil. Stir in the salt and add the macaroni. Cook, stirring occasionally, for 6 to 8 minutes, just until the macaroni is al dente. Drain the macaroni in a colander; do not rinse. In a large bowl, combine the macaroni, cheese sauce, and poblanos. Spoon the mixture into the prepared baking dish.

Evenly scatter the toasted crumbs over the casserole. Bake for 30 minutes, until the mac 'n' cheese is heated through and the top is golden brown and crunchy. Let sit at room temperature for 5 minutes before serving.

BISCUITS AND BREADS

Buttermilk Biscuits with Honey Butter

MAKES TWELVE 2½- TO 3-INCH BISCUITS

HONEY BUTTER

½ cup (1 stick) salted butter

2 tablespoons honey

BISCUITS

2 cups all-purpose flour, plus more for rolling out dough

2 teaspoons baking powder

½ teaspoon baking soda

¾ teaspoon table salt

¼ cup (½ stick) cold salted butter, cubed

1 cup buttermilk

Sourdough starter, a natural yeast mixture, was the leavening of choice for making biscuits and breads on the trail and is still used at the Steakhouse. Using buttermilk, baking powder, and baking soda in place of a starter imparts some of that tangy sourdough flavor to these light biscuits, which are easy to whip up. And oh my, are they good. The secret to great biscuits is to not overwork the dough. Brushing them with honey butter makes them irresistible.

Heat the oven to 450°F.

TO MAKE THE HONEY BUTTER:
Melt the butter in a small saucepan. Pour 1 tablespoon butter into a small dish and reserve it for brushing on the baked biscuits. Stir the honey into the remaining butter and let it melt.

TO MAKE THE BISCUITS: Whisk together the flour, baking powder, baking soda, and salt in a large, shallow bowl. Add the cold butter cubes and use your fingers or a pastry blender to cut it into the flour mixture, making small pea-sized pieces. Add the buttermilk. With a minimum of handling, mix into a smooth dough.

Put the dough on a lightly floured work surface. With a rolling pin, roll out to a generous ½-inch thickness. Using a floured 2½- to 3-inch biscuit cutter, cut the dough into rounds, as close together as possible to avoid having to reroll the dough. Between cutting out the biscuits, dip the cutter into some flour so the dough doesn't stick. Lightly pat together any remaining dough scraps, reroll gently, and cut into additional rounds.

Arrange the biscuits, barely touching, on a baking sheet. Bake until risen and golden brown, about 10 minutes. Lightly brush the tops with the reserved melted butter. Give the warm honey butter a good stir and pour into a small bowl to serve with the biscuits.

CHEDDAR-BLACK PEPPER BISCUITS:
Add 1 teaspoon cracked black pepper to the flour mixture. Reduce the cubed butter to 3 tablespoons. Stir ¾ cup shredded Cheddar in with the wet ingredients. Continue as directed.

Grilled Sourdough Slices with Green Onion Butter

SERVES 8 OR MORE

½ cup (1 stick) salted butter, softened

¼ cup thin-sliced (⅛ inch) green onion tops

1 plump garlic clove, minced

One 1-pound sourdough loaf, unsliced

Since Tom's a bona fide cowboy cook, we often make sourdough bread at the Steakhouse. Like the chuck wagon cooks of old, Tom has kept a crock of sourdough starter alive for years. But he doesn't sleep with it the way the "cookies" on the range did (to ensure that cold weather didn't kill off the yeast and bacteria that would leaven bread, biscuits, and flapjacks). It's a fairly lengthy process to get a sourdough starter—well—started. After that, you need to care for it as you would any living thing, keeping it fed, exercised, and made to feel useful by putting it to work regularly. When making any dough or batter with sourdough, the starter is mixed with new flour and liquid, allowed to ferment and rise, and then some of that dough is mixed back into the starter crock.

We realize not everyone is devoted to caring for a sourdough starter like Tom is, and these days it's easy to find quality sourdough bread at bakeries. To make one of our very favorite ways to enjoy sourdough, buy a quality loaf at your favorite bakery or grocery and grill some slices when you have other food over the fire.

In a bowl, mash together the butter, green onion tops, and garlic. Refrigerate the green onion butter until firm, about 1 hour. When you are ready to use the butter, let it sit at room temperature for 20 to 30 minutes.

You have a few grilling options: You can put the bread slices around the cooler edges of a hot fire; over the cooler side of a two-level fire; or over a medium-heat fire (4 to 5 seconds with the hand test—see page 81) used for grilling vegetables. If grilling over gas or charcoal, add several mesquite chunks to the fire shortly before placing the bread on the grill.

Cut the sourdough bread into 1-inch-thick slices. Toast the bread on the grill on each side for 1 to 2 minutes, until lightly browned, with grill marks. Immediately slather one side of each slice with the onion butter. Serve right away as the butter is melting into the slices, so each bite is soft as well as crunchy.

BREAD CRUMBS

We always have plenty of leftover sourdough bread around the restaurant kitchen. Rather than toss it, we make our own version of large, flaky panko-style bread crumbs Take four or so large, thick slices of day-old bread and brush them generously with olive oil. Put them on a baking sheet and bake at 350°F for about 20 minutes, turning the bread once halfway through. The bread is ready when deeply golden brown. Once the bread cools, use the large-hole side of a cheese grater to make coarse crumbs.

Gingerbread

MAKES 4 OR 5
MINI LOAVES

Vegetable oil spray

2 cups all-purpose flour

One 1-pound box dark brown sugar (2¼ packed cups)

¾ cup (1½ sticks) salted butter, at room temperature

1 teaspoon baking soda

2 teaspoons ground cinnamon

1 teaspoon ground nutmeg

½ teaspoon ground ginger

1 cup buttermilk

2 large eggs

Visitors who stay overnight in our Perini Ranch Guest Quarters will find small loaves of streusel-topped gingerbread as a welcome winter indulgence. These make the best gifts or party favors. If you prefer to make one large loaf in a 9 x 5-inch pan, add about 10 minutes to the baking time.

Heat the oven to 375°F. Spray five mini loaf pans (approximately 3½ x 5½ inches) with vegetable oil spray. We've found pan sizes to be a bit inconsistent. If yours are slightly larger than specified, you may just get four loaves.

Whisk together the flour and brown sugar in a large bowl. Using your fingers, work in the butter until the mixture is crumbly. Scoop out 1 cup of the mixture and set aside to use as a topping.

To the flour mixture in the bowl, add the baking soda, cinnamon, nutmeg, and ginger.

Whisk together the buttermilk and

eggs in a small bowl. Using the whisk, mix the wet ingredients into the dry until well combined. Divide the batter among the prepared pans.

Bake for 10 minutes, then quickly sprinkle the loaves with the reserved topping. Return the pans to the oven and continue baking for 8 to 10 minutes longer, until a toothpick inserted in the centers comes out clean.

Run a dinner knife around the inside of each pan and pop out each loaf. Place them top up on a wire baking rack to cool. Slice and serve. Wrap extra loaves in zippered freezer bags and keep at room temperature for a couple of days, or in the freezer for up to a month.

From left to right: The Supper Club by Perini Ranch (private dining space for up to 40 guests), The Gap Café, Salty Roan Bake House, and the Buffalo Gap Chamber of Commerce.

Skillet Cornbread

SERVES 6 TO 8

Vegetable oil spray

2 cups buttermilk

2 large eggs

2 to 3 drops pure vanilla extract

2 cups stone-ground
yellow cornmeal

2 tablespoons sugar (optional)

1½ teaspoons table salt

1 teaspoon baking soda

¼ cup (½ stick) salted butter,
melted

There's something so darned familiar and satisfying about a cast-iron skillet of cornbread, kind of like slipping into your favorite old flannel shirt. Serve it with chili or any barbecue. Our favorite summer dinner is a bowl of black-eyed peas and a plate of sliced tomatoes from the garden and some skillet cornbread. If you think that sugar only belongs in iced tea, by all means omit it.

Heat the oven to 450°F. Spray an 8-inch cast-iron skillet with vegetable oil spray. Put the skillet in the oven to heat while preparing the cornbread.

Whisk together the buttermilk, eggs, and vanilla in a mixing bowl. In a separate bowl, combine the cornmeal, sugar (if using), salt, and baking soda.

Add the buttermilk mixture and melted butter to the dry ingredients and stir just until combined. Pour the batter into the hot skillet.

Bake for 15 to 18 minutes, until just firm and golden brown on top. Let the bread cool for 5 minutes before slicing into wedges.

Cheddar-Jalapeño Cornbread

SERVES 8

Vegetable oil spray

4 jalapeños

2 cups stone-ground yellow cornmeal

½ cup all-purpose flour

3 tablespoons sugar

4 teaspoons table salt

1 teaspoon baking soda

¼ teaspoon baking powder

2 cups whole milk

2 large eggs

8 ounces (2 cups) shredded Cheddar

2 tablespoons salted butter, melted

Here's a moister, spicier cornbread. It's not as hot as you might guess from the quantity of jalapeños because the cheese and milk douse some of the heat. Jalapeños are so ubiquitous in Texas food today that it may be surprising to realize that they weren't commonly associated with Tex-Mex or other local dishes until the 1960s, about the time that Texan Lyndon B. Johnson succeeded John F. Kennedy as president in 1963. All things Texas enjoyed a burst of recognition, from barbecued brisket to the hot little chile, originally from the Mexican state of Veracruz, known as the jalapeño.

Heat the oven to 325°F. Spray a shallow 9x13-inch baking dish with vegetable oil spray.

Spear the jalapeños on a large fork and hold them over the flame of a gas stove burner. Turn until all sides are blackened and blistered. Immediately put the peppers into a plastic bag, seal, and let them steam and cool for 5 minutes. (If you don't have a gas stove, grill or broil the jalapeños as directed on page 130.)

While the jalapeños cool, whisk together the cornmeal, flour, sugar, salt, baking soda, and baking powder in a large bowl.

Pull off any skin that is loose, but otherwise leave the blackened skin in place to add a little deeper flavor to the cornbread. Seed and mince the jalapeños. Whisk together the jalapeños, milk, and eggs in a bowl. Stir the wet ingredients into the dry, just until combined. Don't overmix. Gently stir in the Cheddar. Pour into the prepared baking dish.

Bake for 40 to 45 minutes, until golden on top and a toothpick inserted into the center comes out clean. Set the dish on a wire baking rack and brush the top of the cornbread with the melted butter. Let sit for 5 minutes. Slice and serve warm or at room temperature.

Zucchini-Pecan Bread

MAKES 1 LOAF

Vegetable oil spray

1 cup sugar

1 cup all-purpose flour

½ teaspoon baking powder

¼ teaspoon baking soda

½ teaspoon ground cinnamon

½ teaspoon table salt

2 large eggs

¾ cup vegetable oil

2 teaspoons pure vanilla extract

2 cups packed shredded zucchini (about ½ pound)

½ cup chopped pecans

On the corner of Litel Street and FM 89 in Buffalo Gap, you'll notice a little rock house on the right—the Perini Ranch Country Market. Park in the back and come on in. We offer everything from old-fashioned toys to our steak rub to fresh, seasonal produce from local farmers. During the summer and fall, we also sell our popular zucchini-pecan loaves. Enjoy as is, or toast slices and spread them with a little butter.

Heat the oven to 325°F. Spray a 9x5x3-inch loaf pan with vegetable oil spray.

Stir together the sugar, flour, baking powder, baking soda, cinnamon, and salt in a bowl.

Put the eggs in a bowl and whisk well. Add the oil and vanilla and beat to combine well. Add the dry ingredients in three additions, mixing well between each one. Add the zucchini and stir well. Fold in the nuts. Pour the batter into the prepared pan.

Bake for 45 to 50 minutes, until a toothpick inserted in the center comes out clean. Cool in the pan for 10 minutes, then turn out onto a wire baking rack covered with a clean dishtowel to avoid indentations. Let the bread cool for at least 20 minutes before slicing. The bread can be served warm or at room temperature.

DESSERTS

Sourdough Bread Pudding with Bourbon Sauce

SERVES 8 TO 10

BREAD PUDDING

Vegetable oil spray

2 large eggs

2½ cups whole milk

2 tablespoons salted butter, melted

2 tablespoons pure vanilla extract

1½ cups sugar

4 packed cups 1-inch-cubed sourdough bread (day-old bread is fine)

⅓ cup chopped pecans

BOURBON SAUCE

½ cup (1 stick) salted butter

½ cup heavy whipping cream

½ cup sugar

¼ cup bourbon

Back in the 1980s, Tom was planning to attend the Chuckwagon Cook-Off at New Mexico's Lincoln County Cowboy Symposium—a major event in ranching culture. The cook-off was offering an unheard-of $3,000 prize for the best dish. Tom knew it would take something different than the usual chuck wagon fare to snag first place. He developed this bread pudding using sourdough bread in a Dutch oven. He added Texas pecans and topped the pudding with a rich, bourbon-laced sauce. Tom won the day and the prize money. This dessert has been on our menu every day since and is our bestseller.

Heat the oven to 325°F. Spray a 9- or 10-inch square baking dish with vegetable oil spray.

TO MAKE THE PUDDING: Whisk the eggs until lightly beaten, then add the milk, melted butter, and vanilla Gradually add the sugar and continue to whisk until the sugar has dissolved.

Arrange the bread cubes in the baking dish. Pour the egg-milk mixture over the bread. Press down on the bread lightly, just enough to make sure all the bread cubes are saturated. Sprinkle the pecans over the bread, lightly pushing them down into the bread as well.

Bake the bread pudding for about 50 minutes, until golden and crusty, but still moist below the top crust.

TO MAKE THE SAUCE: While the pudding bakes, combine the butter, cream, sugar, and bourbon in a saucepan. Bring to a boil, stirring occasionally, and then remove from the heat.

Serve the warm pudding in bowls, topped with a healthy drizzle of the warm sauce.

Tres Leches Cake

SERVES 12 OR MORE

One 18.25-ounce plain yellow cake mix, preferably Duncan Hines, prepared according to package directions and baked in a 9x13-inch cake pan

One 14-ounce can sweetened condensed milk

One 12-ounce can evaporated milk

¾ cup whole milk

Vegetable oil spray

1 pint (2 cups) heavy whipping cream

2 tablespoons confectioners' sugar

Raspberries or other berries (optional)

A relatively recent import from Mexico and Latin America, *tres leches* refers to three milks—sweetened condensed, evaporated, and whole—that are combined and allowed to soak into a baked yellow cake, making it soft and super silky. We added it to our repertoire when we hosted a party in honor of Tom's daughter Jessica, with the theme of *A Night in Old Mexico*, inspired by a trip to San Miguel de Allende. A July night can be hot enough to melt butter on the sidewalk, so we wanted something that would be refreshing. We used a cake mix for ease and simplicity. The whipped cream topping cuts some of the sweetness of this crowd-pleasing, luscious dessert. Berries on the side are welcome, but not a necessity.

While the cake is still warm, gently prick it all over with a fork about every ½ inch. Put the condensed, evaporated, and whole milks in a bowl and mix. Slowly pour the milk mixture over the cake, saturating it evenly and thoroughly. Let the cake sit at room temperature for 30 minutes to cool. Cover the cake with plastic wrap sprayed with vegetable oil spray. Refrigerate for 30 to 60 minutes.

While the cake is chilling, combine the cream and confectioners' sugar in the bowl of a stand mixer with the whisk attachment. Beat on high speed until stiff peaks form. Uncover the cake and spread the whipped cream on top. Cover the cake again and return to the refrigerator for at least 1 hour, or up to 12 hours. Slice and serve with berries, if desired.

Pear-Cranberry Crisp

SERVES 8

TOPPING

½ cup all-purpose flour

½ cup packed brown sugar

¼ cup chopped pecans

½ teaspoon ground cinnamon

¼ cup (½ stick) salted butter, cubed, at room temperature

4 large ripe pears, preferably Anjou or Bartlett

4 ounces fresh or thawed frozen cranberries

4 teaspoons granulated sugar

Designed to serve eight people, this winter dessert has a nice festive feel to it. We cut four pears in half, pack cranberries into the cavities, and scatter a nutty crisp topping over each half.

Heat the oven to 375°F. Butter a 9-inch square baking dish.

TO MAKE THE TOPPING: Combine the flour, brown sugar, pecans, and cinnamon in a food processor. Give the processor a couple of pulses to combine a bit. Add the butter and pulse until the mixture is an evenly crumbly meal.

Peel the pears, then slice each lengthwise in half and core. If the pear halves are roly-poly, slice a very thin bit off each rounded side so they sit still in the baking dish. Place the pears in the dish, cut side up. Mound one-eighth of the cranberries in the hollow of each pear half and sprinkle each with ½ teaspoon granulated sugar.

Spoon the topping over the pears evenly, mounding it over each pear and packing it down lightly. Scatter any remaining cranberries and topping around the pears. Bake the crisp for 40 to 45 minutes, until the topping is crunchy and the pears and cranberries are tender. Serve warm.

CHIVALRY ISN'T DEAD

Lisa wants you to know a story Tom wouldn't tell you himself. He became a rock star at the 2014 James Beard Foundation Awards at New York's Lincoln Center. We were both incredibly honored and excited to find out that the Steakhouse was going to receive one of a handful of awards given each year to America's Classics, restaurants with a timeless sense of place and impeccable food that fits their locale. Unknown to Lisa, Tom had called the Foundation to ask if it might be possible to receive two medallions, feeling Lisa was as much a part of the success as he was. They said no, it could only be one, and since Tom was the founder, they would give the Olympic-type medallion to him. Onstage that night, Tom asked Lisa to hold his cowboy hat (yes, of course, he wore a cowboy hat with his tux). She thought it was to get the medallion hung around his neck, but what he did was hang the medallion around her neck. The crowd of 2,000 went wild with his act of generosity and love. Every woman in Lincoln Center must have come up to Tom afterward to exclaim about his kindness. Eventually Lisa had to hustle him out before someone tried to elope with him.

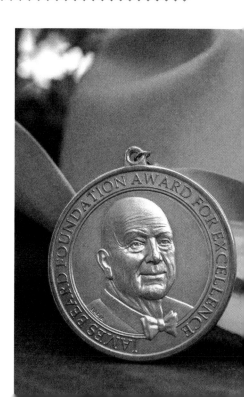

The President's Pecan Pie

SERVES 8 TO 10

SINGLE-CRUST BUTTER-AND-LARD PIE DOUGH

1¼ cups all-purpose flour, plus more for rolling out

½ teaspoon table salt

3 tablespoons salted butter, cut into cubes and chilled

5 tablespoons lard, cut into cubes and chilled

2 to 4 tablespoons ice water

Vegetable oil spray

PECAN FILLING

4 large eggs, lightly beaten

1 cup light corn syrup

⅔ cup sugar

3 tablespoons salted butter, melted

1 tablespoon pure vanilla extract

1½ generous cups coarsely chopped pecans

The most important pecan dish in Lone Star culture and cuisine is pecan pie. Our ranch, like much of Texas, is dotted with pecan trees, and we use pecans in everything from salads to spiced nuts. Lisa tested ten different pie recipes to find the one that appealed to us the most. It's intentionally not a trendy version with some load of chocolate or pumpkin or salted caramel. It's just a classic pie, and not tooth-achingly sweet. We have been very fortunate to cater for the Bush family at the Texas Governor's Mansion in Austin, and later while George W. Bush and First Lady Laura were in the White House and at their Texas homes. President Bush is very fond of this version of every Texan's favorite pie.

TO MAKE THE PIE DOUGH: Combine the flour and salt in a food processor and pulse briefly. Scatter the butter over the flour and pulse three or four times just to combine. Scatter the lard over the flour-butter mixture. Pulse several more times until the fats disappear into the flour. Sprinkle in 2 tablespoons ice water and pulse several times, just until the water is absorbed and the dough comes together.

Dump the dough onto a floured surface. Lightly rub the dough with your fingers, adding more water, 1 tablespoon at a time, as needed just to hold it together. Once the dough holds together, stop. Don't overwork the dough. Gently pat the dough into a 6-inch disk. Wrap in plastic wrap and refrigerate for at least 30 minutes or overnight.

Spray a 9-inch pie pan with vegetable oil spray. Roll out the dough on a floured surface into a thin 12-inch round. Fit the round into the prepared pie pan, avoiding stretching it. Crimp the edges, then refrigerate the crust for at least 15 minutes.

Heat the oven to 375°F.

TO MAKE THE FILLING: Whisk together the eggs, corn syrup, sugar, butter, and vanilla in a bowl. Using a spatula, fold in the pecans. Pour the filling into the pie crust.

Bake the pie for 10 minutes, then reduce the temperature to 350°F. Bake for 35 to 40 minutes longer, until a toothpick inserted into the center comes out clean. Let the pie cool on a wire baking rack for at least 1 hour before slicing and serving.

Pecan Bars

CRUST

Vegetable oil spray

2 cups all-purpose flour

½ cup granulated sugar

¼ teaspoon table salt

¾ cup (1½ sticks) salted butter, cubed and at room temperature

PECAN FILLING

3 large eggs

¾ cup packed light brown sugar

¾ cup light corn syrup

6 tablespoons (¾ stick) salted butter

1 teaspoon pure vanilla extract

2 cups finely chopped pecans

P acked with even more pecans than the preceding pie, these bar cookies work when finger food makes a better finish to a meal than a plated piece of gooey pie requiring a fork. We often serve these side-by-side with the Lemon-Rosemary Bars (page 169).

TO MAKE THE CRUST: Heat the oven to 300°F. Spray a 9-inch square baking dish with vegetable oil spray.

Combine the flour, granulated sugar, and salt in a food processor and pulse three or four times. Sprinkle the butter cubes on top of the flour mixture. Pulse until the dough is crumbly and holds together when pinched with your fingers. Put the dough into the prepared baking dish and use your fingers to press it into an even layer.

Bake for 15 to 20 minutes, until the crust is set and lightly browned. Leave the oven on.

TO MAKE THE FILLING: Beat the eggs in the bowl of a stand mixer. In a saucepan, combine the brown sugar, corn syrup, and butter and bring to a boil over medium-high heat. Remove from the heat and stir in the vanilla. Pour one-quarter of the brown sugar mixture into the eggs and beat for 15 seconds, just to combine. With the mixer running on medium, drizzle in the rest of the brown sugar mixture. Stop the mixer. Using a spatula, fold in the pecans.

Pour the filling over the crust. Bake for 25 to 30 minutes, until the filling is set. Let cool slightly. While still warm, run a table knife around the inside of the pan to loosen the bars, then let cool completely. Cut into squares.

Opposite: Pecan Bars, left, with Lemon-Rosemary Bars.

Lemon-Rosemary Bars

MAKES 16

CRUST

Vegetable oil spray

2 cups all-purpose flour

½ cup sifted confectioners' sugar

2 tablespoons finely chopped fresh rosemary leaves

¼ teaspoon table salt

¾ cup (1½ sticks) salted butter, cubed and at room temperature

LEMON FILLING

¼ cup plus 2 tablespoons all-purpose flour

1½ cups granulated sugar

¾ teaspoon baking powder

3 large eggs

2 tablespoons grated lemon zest

½ cup fresh lemon juice

1 tablespoon confectioners' sugar, for sprinkling

These bar cookies are a slightly more sophisticated take on the bake sale classic, lemon squares. The hint of rosemary adds an interesting twist.

TO MAKE THE CRUST: Heat the oven to 350°F. Spray a 9-inch square pan with vegetable oil spray.

Combine the flour, confectioners' sugar, rosemary, and salt in a food processor and pulse three or four times. Sprinkle the butter cubes on top of the flour mixture. Pulse until the dough is crumbly and holds together when pinched with your fingers. Put the dough into the prepared baking sheet and use your fingers to press it into an even layer.

Bake for 16 to 18 minutes, until the crust is just set and barely colored. Leave the oven on, but reduce the heat to 325°F.

TO MAKE THE FILLING: Whisk together the flour, granulated sugar, and baking powder in a large bowl. Whisk the eggs in a medium bowl. Add the lemon zest and juice to the eggs and whisk until well combined. Slowly stir the egg mixture into the flour mixture. Evenly pour the filling over the crust.

Bake for 20 to 25 minutes, until the filling is lightly set. Let cool slightly. While still warm, run a table knife around the inside of the pan to loosen the bars, then let cool completely. Cut into squares. Sprinkle with confectioners' sugar just before serving.

Tom's Great-Grandmother's Strawberry Shortcake

SERVES 8

SUGAR BISCUITS

2 cups all-purpose flour, plus more for rolling out

⅓ cup sugar, plus more for sprinkling

2 teaspoons baking powder

½ teaspoon baking soda

¾ teaspoon table salt

¼ cup (½ stick) salted butter

1 cup buttermilk

1 tablespoon salted butter, melted, for brushing

STRAWBERRIES

2 pound fresh strawberries, green tops removed, halved vertically, and any white centers removed

½ cup sugar

1 cup heavy whipping cream

This shortcake, handed down through Tom's family for generations, started with his great-grandmother Becky Blake, from Abilene. In her day, people grew their own fragile little berries that never would have made it to a supermarket. These days, strawberries are bred for sturdiness instead of flavor, but by macerating them in sugar and then warming them gently, every bit of sweetness can be coaxed out. Paired with a sweet biscuit and a bowl of cream, this is heaven. This was and still is the birthday dessert of choice for many Perini family members!

TO MAKE THE BISCUITS: Heat the oven to 450°F. Line a baking sheet with parchment paper or a silicone baking mat.

Stir together the flour, sugar, baking powder, baking soda, and salt in a large shallow bowl. Cut in the butter with the back of large fork, incorporating it until pea-sized. Pour in the buttermilk and, using your hands, mix with a minimum of strokes into a smooth dough. Lightly flour a work surface, transfer the dough to it, and roll out to a generous ½-inch thickness. Using a floured 3-inch biscuit cutter, cut the dough into rounds, as close together as possible to avoid having to reroll the dough. Between cutting out the biscuits, dip the cutter into some flour so the dough doesn't stick. Lightly pat together any remaining dough scraps, reroll gently, and cut into rounds. (If you end up with more than eight biscuits, you have a cook's treat.)

Transfer the biscuits to a baking sheet. Brush the biscuit tops lightly with the melted butter, then sprinkle with sugar. Bake, rotating the pan after 10 minutes, for 18 to 20 minutes total, until the biscuits are raised and golden brown.

TO PREPARE THE STRAWBERRIES: Meanwhile, combine the strawberries with the sugar in a medium saucepan. Let sit for 15 minutes for the juices to come to the surface. Warm over medium heat until the juices begin to thicken.

TO SERVE: Halve the biscuits and arrange each bottom on a dessert plate. Using half of the strawberries, spoon equal amounts over the biscuit bottoms. Place the top half of each biscuit over the berries, then spoon the remaining berries equally over the biscuit tops. Serve right away with cream poured over and around each portion.

Banana Pudding

½ cup sugar

1 tablespoon cornstarch

¼ teaspoon kosher salt

3 large egg yolks

¾ cup whole milk

½ cup half-and-half

1½ teaspoons pure
vanilla extract

4 ounces (1 cup) Cool Whip
whipped topping, thawed

18 vanilla wafer cookies,
plus 6 cookies for serving

2 medium bananas

This childhood favorite delights diners of all ages. We serve it in half-pint mason jars with the metal ring screwed on for a touch of nostalgia. If you're planning to take the pudding jars to a picnic or other event, put on the lids as well. Slice the bananas just before serving so they don't turn brown. For big parties, we nestle the jars in a big galvanized metal tub of ice so everyone can help themselves. We use Cool Whip, because it holds its height much better than whipped cream.

Stir together the sugar, cornstarch, and salt in a heavy saucepan. Whisk in the egg yolks, followed by the milk and half-and-half. Cook the pudding over medium-low heat, stirring frequently, until thick enough to coat the back of a spoon. It will take 15 to 20 minutes for the pudding to thicken. Remove the pudding from the heat and stir in the vanilla.

Using a spatula, fold in the Cool Whip by hand until there are no streaks. Refrigerate the pudding for up to an hour. To store the pudding for up to a day, place a piece of plastic wrap directly on the pudding's surface to prevent a skin from forming.

Put the 18 cookies in a zippered plastic bag and finely crush with a rolling pin. Set aside ½ cup cookie crumbs. Sprinkle equal portions of the remaining crumbs in the bottoms of 6 glasses. Spoon about ½ cup chilled pudding into each jar. Stand 1 whole cookie in the center of each pudding.

Peel and slice the bananas. Top each pudding serving with some banana slices, then sprinkle on the remaining cookie crumbs. Serve immediately.

Peach-Bourbon Cobbler

SERVES 8 OR MORE

DOUBLE-CRUST BUTTER-AND-LARD PIE DOUGH

2½ cups all-purpose flour, plus more for rolling

1 teaspoon table salt

8 tablespoons (1 stick) salted butter, cut into cubes and chilled

8 tablespoons lard, cut into cubes and chilled

6 to 8 tablespoons ice water

Vegetable oil spray

PEACH FILLING

¾ cup (1½ sticks) salted butter

2 to 2½ pounds fresh or frozen peaches, peeled, pitted, and thinly sliced

1 cup heavy whipping cream

¾ cup packed brown sugar

½ cup granulated sugar, plus additional for sprinkling over the top

¾ teaspoon ground cinnamon, plus additional for sprinkling over the top

⅓ cup bourbon

Peaches from Central Texas are one of early summer's fleeting treats, and cobbler is the way we most often present them. A splash of bourbon makes a fine addition to the juicy filling. Note that this cobbler is made with a double batch of butter-and-lard pie dough—half the dough lines the pan, the other goes over the filling. Feel free to use your own favorite pie dough recipe. If you don't have access to fresh peaches, frozen ones are the next best choice. Top the warm cobbler with a scoop of vanilla ice cream, if desired.

TO MAKE THE PIE DOUGH: Combine the flour and salt in a food processor and pulse briefly. Scatter the butter over the flour and pulse three or four times just to combine. Scatter the lard over the flour-butter mixture. Pulse several more times until the fats disappear into the flour. Sprinkle in 6 tablespoons ice water and pulse several times, just until the water is absorbed and the dough comes together.

Dump the dough onto a floured surface. Lightly rub the dough with your fingers, adding more water, 1 tablespoon at a time, as needed just to hold it together. Once the dough holds together, stop. Don't overwork the dough. Divide the dough into two equal pieces. Gently pat each piece into a 6-inch disk. Wrap in plastic wrap and refrigerate for at least 30 minutes or overnight.

Heat the oven to 400°F. Spray a 9x13-inch baking dish with vegetable oil spray.

On a lightly floured surface, roll each dough piece into a 9x13-inch rectangle. Fit one rectangle in the bottom of the dish. Bake for 18 to 20 minutes, until lightly set. Remove the pan from the oven. Leave the oven on, but reduce the temperature to 350°F.

TO MAKE THE FILLING: While the bottom crust is baking, melt the butter in a large saucepan. Stir in the peaches, cream, brown sugar, granulated sugar, and cinnamon and bring to a boil over high heat. Reduce the heat to low and simmer for 15 minutes, or until the peaches are tender. Stir in the bourbon and cook for another couple of minutes. Evenly pour the filling over the bottom crust. Top with the second dough rectangle, tucking the edges in. Using a knife, cut four to six 1- to 2-inch slits in the top dough so steam can escape. Sprinkle the top lightly with sugar and cinnamon.

Bake the cobbler for 40 to 45 minutes, until the top crust is crisp and golden. Let the cobbler sit for 15 minutes before serving.

Jalapeño Cheesecake

CRUST

¾ cup graham cracker crumbs

¾ cup chopped pecans

¼ cup sugar

¼ cup (½ stick) salted butter, at room temperature

FILLING

1 jalapeño, quartered and seeded

Three 8-ounce packages (1½ pounds) cream cheese

½ cup sugar

1 tablespoon fresh lemon juice

1 teaspoon pure vanilla extract

3 large eggs

TOPPING

1 cup (8 ounces) sour cream

1 tablespoon sugar

1 tablespoon fresh lemon juice

Jalapeño jelly, for serving

1 whole pickled jalapeño per slice, optional

Along with our bread pudding, this cheesecake is our most popular dessert at the Steakhouse. The combination of heat and sweet surprises many diners. When they have trouble imagining it, we often mention the favorite Texas appetizer of pepper jelly on cream cheese, and the light bulb goes on. We top each slice, before it heads to a table, with a whole pickled jalapeño. Feel free to do the same if you have a flair for the dramatic.

Heat the oven to 350°F.

TO MAKE THE CRUST: Combine the graham cracker crumbs, pecans, and sugar in a food processor. Pulse in rapid bursts until the mixture is smooth. Add the butter and pulse until the butter is absorbed. Pour the crumb mixture into a 10-inch springform pan. Using your fingers or the back of a spoon, firmly press the crust smoothly on the bottom and about 1 inch up the sides of the pan. Bake the crust for 10 minutes. Remove from the oven and let cool for 5 minutes.

TO MAKE THE FILLING: Pulse the jalapeño in the food processor to mince. Add the cream cheese, sugar, lemon juice, and vanilla and blend until smooth. Add the eggs and mix again until combined. Pour the filling into the crust. Using a spatula, smooth the top. Bake the cheesecake for 1 hour, until the center is just set.

TO MAKE THE TOPPING: While the cheesecake is baking, whisk together the sour cream, sugar, and lemon juice in a small bowl.

When the cheesecake is done, remove from the oven and evenly spread on the topping. Return the cheesecake to the oven for an additional 10 minutes, or until the topping has set. Cool completely on a wire baking rack. Cover and refrigerate for at least 3 hours, or up to overnight.

To serve, slice the cake with a knife that has been dipped in hot water. Spoon 1 to 2 tablespoons jalapeño jelly over each slice before serving.

A CAKE OF CHEESES

||||||||||||||||||||||||||||||||||||||||

One of our most remarked-upon presentations for a wedding was not a conventional cake, or even a cheesecake, per se, but a cake of cheese. At the request of the bride and groom, we put together a six-layer extravaganza with side garnishes of Italian *salume*. The round cheeses were set on top of each other in decreasing size, just like a tiered wedding cake. At the bottom was a nutty rosemary Asiago followed by a six-month aged Piave. Next came a classic Basque sheep's milk Ossau Iraty AOC followed by a Brie Couronne coated with cracked black pepper. Another Brie, a slightly milder, sweeter Martin-Collet Petit Brie, came next. Topping it all was a Chaource with the aroma of mushrooms and cream. The accompanying cured meats included beef bresaola, pork sopressa Veneta, *finocchiona* (fennel-infused) *salume*, and a smoky speck, or ham, from the southern Alps.

Texas Chocolate Sheet Cake

SERVES 16 OR MORE

CAKE

Vegetable oil spray

1 cup (2 sticks) salted butter

¼ cup unsweetened cocoa

2 cups all-purpose flour

2 cups granulated sugar

2 large eggs, beaten lightly

½ cup buttermilk

1 teaspoon pure vanilla extract

1 teaspoon baking soda

½ teaspoon ground cinnamon

FROSTING

¼ cup (1 stick) salted butter

¼ cup unsweetened cocoa

¼ cup plus 2 tablespoons whole milk

1 pound (3½ cups) confectioners' sugar, plus additional for serving

1 teaspoon pure vanilla extract

1 cup chopped pecans

Just about every heritage cookbook published by a Junior League, a family, or a historical society in Texas includes a version of this fudgy treat. Much of its appeal to Texans is its sheer size, since it's baked on a large baking sheet rather than in round cake pans. Both the cake and the frosting should be warm when you put them together. The cake easily cuts into squares, feeds a crowd, and travels well, making it a great choice for picnics, birthdays, anniversaries, or any celebration.

This particular version was popularized in the 1960s by Texan Lady Bird Johnson, First Lady of the United States, when Lyndon Baines Johnson was president.

TO MAKE THE CAKE: Heat the oven to 350°F. Spray a 13x18-inch rimmed baking sheet with vegetable oil spray.

Melt the butter in a large saucepan over medium heat. Remove the pan from the heat and add 1 cup water and the cocoa, stirring well. Whisk together the flour and granulated sugar in a bowl, then whisk into the chocolate mixture. Whisk together the eggs, buttermilk, vanilla, baking soda, and cinnamon in a mixing bowl. Pour the chocolate-flour mixture into the egg-buttermilk mixture and whisk again until well combined.

Pour the cake batter onto the baking sheet, spreading it evenly. Bake for 18 to 20 minutes, rotating the baking sheet from back to front once after about 10 minutes. When the cake is done, a toothpick inserted into the center will come out clean.

TO MAKE THE FROSTING: While the cake is baking, melt the butter with the cocoa in a large saucepan over medium heat. Add the milk and bring just to a boil. Whisk in the confectioners' sugar, stirring well to eliminate any clumps. Remove the frosting from the heat and use a spatula to fold in the vanilla and pecans. Immediately pour the thin frosting over the warm cake, spreading it quickly and evenly. Cool completely, then slice to serve.

TEXAS ROYALTY

||||||||||||||||||||||||||||||||||

It has been our honor to cater for the Bush family at the Texas Governor's Mansion, the White House, and their ranch in Crawford. While President George W. Bush has long been a big fan of The President's Pecan Pie (page 165), he became even more excited about our Texas Chocolate Sheet Cake. When Laura Bush spoke with Lisa about catering the Bushes' joint 70th birthday celebration at their Central Texas ranch, she said that George W. insisted on having the cake. To serve the many guests who would be attending, Lisa came up with the idea of stacking four sheet cakes on top of one another.

Following the meal, we were asked to carry out the cake personally while Texas country music legend George Strait serenaded the guests and then broke out into "Happy Birthday." It was all quite festive, but never did we dream that escorting the cake would land us on the pages of *People* magazine.

Dinner Celebrating
the 70th Birthdays of
President and Mrs. George W. Bush

Avocado and Grapefruit Salad

Mesquite-Smoked Peppered Beef Tenderloin
Southern Fried Catfish
Roasted Corn and Poblano Pudding
Green Beans
Bourbon Carrots
Cheddar and Black Pepper Biscuits

Texas Chocolate Sheet Cake

Prairie Chapel Ranch
Crawford, Texas
October 22, 2016

*Camp House at Perini
Ranch Guest Quarters*

ACKNOWLEDGMENTS *A note from Lisa*

Well, it's been twenty years since *Texas Cowboy Cooking* (Tom's first book) was released, and the inside story is that I have said, for nineteen years, "If there's another book, there will have to be another woman in your life, because I can't do that again." It was a hard process. So, as talk progressed and the need became stronger for another book, of course I had to recant my famous claim.

And, I will tell you all that this process has been a joy. The partners involved in the project were an absolute pleasure to work with and not only have we had fun, strengthened friendships, and eaten lots of great food from testing recipes, I, and our team, have learned so much. I wouldn't trade this process for anything. I told Tom that I've had more fun at work in 2019 than in a long time!

Never did I think I'd be in business with my husband, but Tom Perini is amazing! His kind, generous spirit sets the tone for every thought and decision that is made at the ranch and I've learned so much from him. He's hard to find during food photography and late-night text edits, but he's always there, with a wide smile and a twinkle in the eye when it's needed. His energy is limitless and the ideas we share for the future are so exciting.

Our first call for help on this project was to our friend Cheryl Jamison. When you have a friend who has an armload of James Beard Awards for cookbooks she's authored, has the best laugh, and lives in one of our favorite cities, it's easy to know who to call. This project has brought us together even more often—always over food and drink—and the process has been a pleasure. Cheryl not only wrote the text, but tested every single recipe for household measurements. Quite a feat! Cheryl's work was made smoother by her administrative assistant, Kathryn Marshall. Cheryl was further aided with home recipe testing by young chef and Santa Fe Community College Culinary Arts graduate Kyle Pacheco. We all wish him the very best of luck in his career in the food world.

Cheryl also brought to us Harriet Bell, one of the country's foremost cookbook editors, who agreed to oversee the project. Despite living in New York City, Harriet embraced the ranch, the Steakhouse, and our vision for this book from our earliest conversations. From squeezing limes for Mesquite-a-Ritas to gently guiding us through the myriad aspects of the publishing process, she was adept at every facet of bringing our book to life.

Our second call was to famed photographer Wyatt McSpadden. Several years ago, he'd taken the portrait of Tom that was on the cover of *Texas Monthly* (see photo on page 13), and we fell in love with his photographic style and with his team. I'm still shocked that he took my call and said yes immediately to this project.

Wyatt and his assistants, Will Phillips and Jeff Stockton, were in Buffalo Gap so many days that we might have to change the population sign, and I hope they know just how pleasurable they made this experience.

We opted to handle photo styling internally as we wanted the food to look like it does here at the ranch. Our management team did an exceptional job; Dale Cronk and Suzanne Travis worked tirelessly. They were joined by Jason Mayes, Dustin Kruse, and Kendra Jenkins, who made all this food happen, and Heather Pate, who took on some of my daily duties so I could work on this project. The rest of our team, too many to mention, were also exceptional: Everyone participated, helped, and covered for us while we were working on the book.

Nancy McMillen, our book designer, brought to this project years of publication design experience, vast talent, and a remarkable ability to visualize and organize the book's content. Truly, she has the most thorough organizational skills we've ever encountered.

We must thank Patricia Sharpe, longtime *Texas Monthly* food editor, for coining "Real Texas Food" to describe us long ago. We're so honored that she chooses to return to the ranch regularly.

And, as always, we are forever grateful to all of our friends in the beef industry who have encouraged, supported, and continued to excite us about the industry. The Texas Beef Council, Texas and Southwest Cattle Raisers Association, and the U.S. Meat Export Federation have been invaluable partners and allow us to travel, advocate, promote, and enjoy U.S. beef across the world. The stories, memories, and friendships are truly valued.

And, finally to our customers—you have supported all aspects of our crazy business and we have all become one big family. We appreciate you so much.

ADDITIONAL PHOTOGRAPHY CREDITS: Page 31: U.S. National Archives and Records Administration; page 175: Sarah Aull/Sarah Kate Photo; page 177: Grant Miller for the George W. Bush Presidential Center.

Index

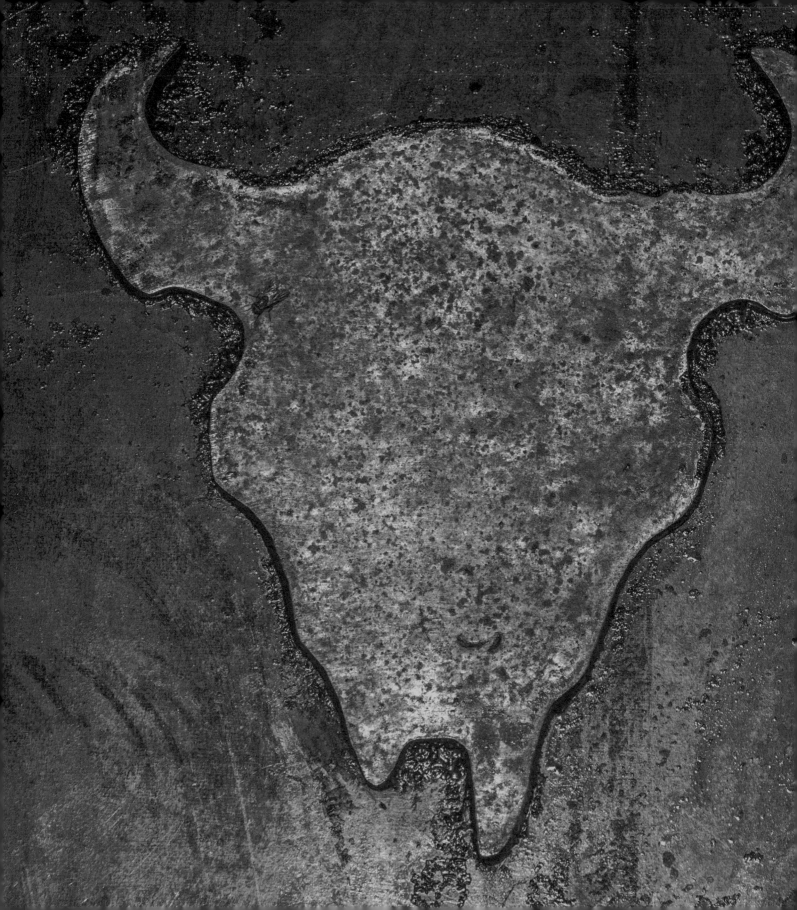